W9-AOM-125

THE TIGER'S WHISKERS

THE TIGER'S WHISKERS

JEAN CARAN

Translated from the French by
FRANCES FRENAYE *and* HAROLD TALBOTT

WALKER AND COMPANY/NEW YORK

Published simultaneously in Canada by George J. McLeod, Limited Toronto.

LIBRARY OF CONGRESS CATALOG CARD NUMBER: 65-15992

First published in the United States of America in 1965 by Walker and Company, a division of Publications Development Corporation.

PRINTED IN THE UNITED STATES OF AMERICA

"Man's heart is iron;
the law is burning coals"
—CHINESE PROVERB

This and all the other Chinese proverbs
are from Dictons Chinois *by Alph. Hubrecht, C.M.*
(Peiping: Lazarist Press, 1933)

THE TIGER'S WHISKERS

I

"If the dragon moves through shallow water the crab mocks him; if the tiger ventures into the plain, the dog laughs at his expense."

—CHINESE PROVERB

Mr. Liu Chi-pan, an enormously rich comprador of the colony of Hong Kong, owed his fortune to his quick-wittedness. Toward the end of the last century, when it was announced that His Royal Highness the Prince of Wales would visit Hong Kong on the occasion of his official tour of Malaya and Australia, Mr. Liu instantly recognized the opportunity to make his fondest dream come true.

By telegram he engaged the services of the most renowned Crown architect, established for him a credit of one hundred and fifty thousand pounds sterling, had bricks brought from Scotland, marble from Carrara, mahogany from the Philippines, and teak from Siam, and, on a flat stretch halfway up the island, built in great haste a little "folly" in Victorian baroque style. While the decorators put the finishing touches on the frescoes in the bathroom and the gardeners planted the last tufts of grass on the terrace, Mr. Liu donned his ceremonial robe. Preceded by his valets in green tunics who cut a path through the crowd, he had himself brought to the governor in his sedan chair.

"Your Excellency, your miserable servant begs to put his unworthy hovel at the disposal of our August Visitor during his glorious sojourn in our humble colony."

It was to be noted shortly afterward in the annual honors list that His Gracious Majesty had deigned to confer a knighthood upon Sir Archibald Liu of Hong Kong.

In 1951, the press correspondents of Hong Kong, those at least who recalled the splendors of the club at Shanghai, from which they had been driven by the revolution, were looking for premises in which to re-establish themselves. The Liu family had been extinct for years, owing to a lack of quick-witted males, and the modest "folly" of Sir Archibald was up for rent. Nobody wanted it, the Chinese because its great reception halls did not lend themselves to family intrigues, the foreign devils because they found it too pretentious, and because it was impossible to air-condition rooms endowed with fifteen-foot ceilings. The correspondents got it at a very low price.

On the tenth of October, 1951, Frank Williams of the International News Agency woke up around ten o'clock with a mild headache and a dry mouth. The weekly club night had ended for him about four in the morning. He had had designs on Suzy Patterson, the traveling correspondent for *Newsweek*. He had made a play for her the whole evening, but that dirty dog Di Cicco of the Rome *Espresso* had finally tricked him out of her. In his annoyance, Frank had gone off to bed.

He decided to get some air on the lawn. He put on his bedroom slippers and a bathrobe and went down the grand staircase of the club. Li, the number three boy, busy waxing the ground-floor ballroom, gave him a good-morning accompanied by a knowing look.

Why so knowing? What did that fellow have to be so gay about today? Frank opened the door, took several steps on the lawn, then headed slowly toward the Italianate balustrade that enclosed the terrace. As he approached, the landscape came into view over the railing. First the line of peaks of the New Territories, extraordinarily clear in the limpid atmosphere of the Chinese autumn; then the city of Kowloon with, at the tip of the peninsula, the great gray mass of the Peninsula Hotel; nearer still, the harbor with its steamers alongside the quay, its cargo ships at anchor, surrounded by tenders and "walla-wallas" (the naval taxis of Hong Kong), its mysterious junks and busy ferries.

Frank lit a cigarette and leaned on the railing. He daydreamed, mindlessly, looking into the distance. Up to the moment when he was shaken by smoker's cough.

"Damn!" He angrily threw his cigarette over the balustrade and watched the course of the butt. From the terrace there was a sheer drop down to the incredible jumble of Chinese houses of Queens Road West. Frank leaned over further and then he *saw*. The sight woke him up completely; his professional instinct did the rest.

He ran to his room on tiptoe, grabbed a pair of binoculars, which he hid under his bathrobe, came back to the balustrade, and watched for a long time. The district was covered with Nationalist flags.

"Man, what a stab in the back!" Still on tiptoe he returned to his room, locked himself in, and as a further precaution placed a blanket folded four times under the typewriter. It was especially important that the noise of the machine, unusual at this hour of the morning, should not wake his colleagues and rivals. He had several hours' lead on them. By the time they had finished sleeping off their alcohol his dispatch would already be spread across the front page of all the papers: "Plebiscite against Mao at Hong Kong."

Kuomintang China celebrates the Double Tenth, that is, the tenth day of the tenth month, the anniversary of the Hankow uprising that precipitated the fall of the Manchu dynasty and the arrival of the Republic in 1911. When the Communists came to power in 1949 they chose for the national holiday October 1, the day of the official founding of the regime at Peking.

On October 1, 1949, the Chinese at Hong Kong patriotically hoisted the flag of the New China. The red flag with five yellow stars was flying everywhere, even in the elegant residential sections, and with even greater reason in the business district. Bursting with pride, the passers-by admired the gigantic pennant atop the new skyscraper of the People's Bank (built with the Nationalists' money) which dwarfed by several stories the Hong Kong Bank of the arrogant capitalists, which had previously towered over the buildings of the colony.

It was the year of victory of the People's Army of Liberation, the year when Heaven's mandate passed to a new dynasty, when President Mao's government, enriched by confiscations, impatient to restore the country's economy after twenty years of uninterrupted fighting, ordered whatever was needed from Hong Kong no matter what the price, with no argument and with payment in advance.

It was also the year in which the debris of the former dynasty, crestfallen and without hope, took refuge in Formosa, just as the Mings had fled from the Manchus three centuries before. And like the Mings the Nationalists would undoubtedly not last long. So it was that the flags of the Kuomintang were missing on the tenth of October.

The year 1950 had amply confirmed the popularity of Peking. The refugees themselves, already numbering more than a million and making up half the population of Hong Kong, prudently decked themselves out in revolutionary colors. This was the honeymoon year of the new regime and the Chinese people, the year of bright tomorrows, of moderation, the year when the Party silently fitted into place the instruments of control.

There was nevertheless a slight shadow across the picture: the Korean war had broken out, the Americans had intervened, MacArthur's forces were rushing upon the Yalu . . . and there was no telling what might happen.

Therefore the flags of Chiang Kai-shek reappeared on the tenth of October. Reappeared very timidly, to be sure (they could be counted on one's fingers); but still it was impossible to deny their presence. The Kuomintang was not altogether dead.

In 1951, a sensational development. While the official Communist agencies without exception, flew the colors and the buildings of the People's Bank, the People's Airline Company, the *Ta Kung Pao* and the other Party newspapers were as brilliantly decorated as usual, there was a noticeable indifference among the people. In the downtown store fronts, in the windows of the populous quarters, on the shanty-town rooftops, flags with five stars were visibly sparse. And on the tenth of October the Nationalist flags made a triumphal return even in the proletarian quarters where there were no refugees.

What had happened was that the inhabitants of Hong Kong had been informed by relatives who had remained in China, by the stories of the last refugees, and by the provincial Communist press, the press not destined for export, which they read with as close attention as the many professional observers, that the honeymoon was over. The corrupting bourgeoisie was being killed off, peasants formerly allies but now "rich landlords, exploiters of the people" were being executed, and the intellectuals, always so turbulent, were being made to toe the line. After the intervention of Chinese volunteers in Korea, the American Seventh Fleet prevented any Communist landing in Formosa and Chiang Kai-Shek's stock automatically went up. As for business dealings with Peking, the Allies had decreed an embargo on strategic products to China, and the Americans, the biggest suppliers and buyers, had in their rage imposed a total embargo. It was the end of the golden age of getting rich quick.

Comrade N'g, in charge of the Hong Kong branch of the Agitprop Bureau of the South China Region, was nervously pacing up and down Platform 2 of the Canton-North station. Everything had gone badly for some time and particularly that morning. For one thing, the ten thirty-seven train from Peking was late and now that idiot Wang, his comrade secretary, had seen fit to bring a bouquet of flowers—at the very height of the Three Antis Campaign—now I ask you!

"The Three Antis, comrade secretary, do you know what they are? Anti-corruption, anti-bureaucracy, anti-waste. Go throw those flowers wherever you like, I don't want them around here at the station." The hick, she had never even seen a telephone before the liberation.

Comrade N'g bit his lip. There he was, harboring wrong thoughts, on account of this melon-head. Divorcing himself from the masses, falling into the deviation of arrogant bourgeois intellectualism.

"One word in the wrong place at this point and I'll be up for reform by hard labor. No question of getting out of it by an easy confession. Too many comrades are waiting for me to make a slip."

Just then the stationmaster came out of his office.

"Hello, Comrade Stationmaster. When is this train showing up? It's already half an hour late."

"No, no, comrade. The train's not late. On the contrary, it will arrive seventeen minutes early."

"Is that so? Then when is that?"

"At three twenty-two this afternoon."

"How come?"

"Because the comrade workers of the Hankow-Canton line, inspired by President Mao Tse-tung and by the heroic exploits of the People's Volunteers in Korea, have exceeded their work norm by 19.64 per cent in the course of the last three months."

"Congratulations, comrade. That's a great triumph."

"I am informed that the timetables have been adapted in such a way as to take account of the new record."

"I get it, Comrade Stationmaster."

Comrade N'g didn't get it at all, but this was neither the time nor the place for discussing railroad work norms. It was Comrade Wu's responsibility, or rather, his successor's, since Wu was at this very moment busily reshaping his wrong views in the tin mines of Yunan.

"No use waiting here, I'll come back this afternoon," N'g decided.

The visitors' bureau had put a car at his disposal for the occasion. It was a Japanese copy of a 1936 Chevrolet. Naturally, the battery had run down. He and the driver pushed it to get it moving. The motor coughed, caught and N'g and the driver jumped onto the running board. N'g had himself dropped off at his office in the former French barracks, next to the Love-the-Masses Hotel on Shameen Island. For the seventh time he reread the telegram from Peking:

> URGENT. TOP SECRET. PEKING, APRIL 10, 1952, 11:26 A.M. FOR AGITPROP SOUTH CHINA CANTON. ATTENTION COMRADE N'G. COMRADE CHANG PO-LIANG UNDERSECRETARY CENTRAL AGITPROP BUREAU WILL ARRIVE CANTON APRIL 12, 10:37 TRAIN.

Chang Po-liang! The terror of the Agitprop cadres! N'g had never met him, but like everyone else he knew his reputation. A protégé of Comrade Vice-President Liu Shao-chi, he had studied medicine at the Aurora university at Shanghai, was a cell leader at the time of the 1927 revolution, was arrested by the reactionaries of the Kuomintang and condemned to death. He escaped from the prison van, rejoined the underground and participated in the Long March; a political commissar for the Eighth Combat Group of the Fourth Route Army, he returned to Shanghai in 1942 to help set up the secret organization; on mission to Moscow from 1946 to 1948 . . . N'g concluded for the seventh time that he'd had it. A train wreck? A convenient air raid by the American imperialists? Things like that never happened when you needed them. N'g had thought at one point of taking advantage of the ruckus during the campaign of the Three Antis to slip out to Hong Kong, but Security had foreseen the gambit. Twenty-six who fled had already been arrested along the Canton-Lowu route and on the way to Macao. It was impossible even to leave the house alone; people always went about in pairs at least, each one responsible for the other. He had had the greatest difficulty convincing Comrade Wang to sneak out of the station with her flowers. She would have to provide a detailed explanation that night of how she had spent the free time between ten-fifteen and noon. Because nothing was let go by at the daily meetings of criticism and self-criticism. That would get the fool moving.

"I've brought you some tea, Comrade N'g." There she was, back again.

"Thank you, comrade secretary. A glass of water will do." What was she thinking of? To drink tea at a moment like this? Why not some Hennessy, as in the good old days? Comrade Chu had been purged because he used too much toilet paper; was N'g going to risk drinking tea? She must be doing it on purpose! Maybe she wasn't as stupid as she looked.

"By the way, comrade secretary, look and see if the Hong Kong paper has come and bring it to me." Thank God he was the only one in his office who could read English. That was precisely how he had managed to be selected for such delicate duties despite his bourgeois origins. When Comrade Wang returned with the *China Mail*, N'g opened it abruptly to page nine and shamelessly immersed himself in the movie reviews, which were his favorite secret relaxation. They were showing a new film at the Empire, with Bill Mayne, called "Incident at Indian Creek." It was three years since N'g had seen a western. Last week the meeting of the study group for agricultural collectivization among the big brothers of the Soviet Union had been replaced by a movie, "The Spy Under the Cassock" and "The Heroine of Sungari," two boring films. If only he had been able to sleep through them. But you had to make an immediate commentary after the showing. And those who had not followed the film were in hot water.

"As soon as the campaign of the Three Antis is over, if I haven't been purged," N'g thought, "I'll suggest to the people in the propaganda film section that they should make use of westerns. Show the masses how the imperialists massacred the defenseless redskins. There'd have to be some cuts, naturally, but it would be better than nothing." Absent-mindedly N'g turned to page one and did a double-take. Big fat lettering spread across the whole front page:

HUGE FIRE AT KAITAK
20,000 HOMELESS

As he read the article, his sullen face grew brighter.

"Comrade Wang," he cried. "Bring me some tea! Yes, tea. Not hot water. And what about the flowers? You've given them to the Young Pioneers? Go get them immediately. Hurry up. I'll wait for you before I set out for the station!"

The People's Security guards stood at attention, the loudspeakers gave out with the *March of the Volunteers,* and the engine, decorated with President Mao's portrait, finally came to a standstill. The loudspeakers announced that Comrade N'g was awaiting his visitor from Peking under the banner "Long Live Peace Between the Peoples of the World."

"Comrade N'g?"

"Exactly, Comrade Undersecretary Chang. Welcome to Canton! This is Comrade Secretary Wang, heroine of the struggle against the local tyrants in the district of Tungku in Honan. I am proud to have her with me to help work for the final victory against the doomed imperialist enemies."

"Comrade N'g, I present to you Comrade Sun, who is accompanying me."

"Comrade Chang, Comrade Wang and I wish to offer you these modest flowers on behalf of the Agitprop Bureau of South China. They are a sign that your visit will mark a decisive turning point in our battle against the imperialists and their running dogs."

"I am unworthy of the honor, Comrade N'g. But I particularly wish to tell you that the Central Bureau is keenly interested in the activity of your branch. It is for this reason that Comrade Sun, who is the assistant chief of the Intelligence Section of National Public Security, made a point of coming with me."

"Comrade Chang, considering the interest so rightly shown by the Central Bureau, and in view of the urgency of the situation, permit me to suggest that we go immediately to my office, in spite of your long and tiring trip."

As soon as they reached the office, and he had washed his face with a hot towel, Chang opened fire. For in the New China people are direct.

"Comrade N'g, six months have gone by since the reactionary agents of the traitor Chiang Kai-shek, openly aided and abetted by their American masters and English lackeys, instituted their outrageous policy of provocation in Hong Kong. The people are infuriated and require just and legitimate reprisal. The workers of Hong Kong do not wish to submit any longer to the insults and affronts of the colonialists while their blood brothers in Free China march with heads high, under the glorious leadership of President Mao, towards progress, dignity and prosperity. I will not . . ."

"My instructions . . ."

"I am aware of your instructions, comrade, I am the one who issued them. You were ordered to act prudently, to be sure, but also forcefully. And don't you tell me that . . ."

"The masses did not cooperate, Comrade Chang. On two occasions . . ."

"The Party does not tolerate tailism in its ranks, comrade. I did not come here to listen to excuses. Comrade N'g, I solemnly ask you, what are you going to do?"

N'g handed the *China Mail* to his visitor. "Read this article, Comrade Chang."

"I do not read the language of the imperialists."

"I will translate it for you. It forms part of my plan.

> "'Around eleven o'clock last night, a huge fire destroyed a squatters area near the Colony airport. Firemen rushed from Kowloon, together with a crew of Royal Air Force technicians, were unable to control the blaze in this highly flammable area. According to police calculations, two thousand five hundred huts were destroyed and twenty thousand people were left without shelter. They have been temporarily relocated in tents provided by the army. No casualties were reported. According to the District Commissioner of Police, the fire was caused by the accidental explosion of a kerosene lamp in a cook-shop."

N'g stopped reading for a moment to emphasize the last sentence with a smile. He resumed:

> "'The mayor of Kowloon went immediately to the district and assured the blaze victims of the full assistance of the authorities and of the charitable organizations for the rebuilding of their homes. As we went to press, bulldozers from the Royal Engineers had gone to work cleaning up the rubble and the inhabitants were being fed with rice and hot food by Civil Defence field kitchens.'

"There you are, comrade. I will now unfold my plan. But it is late. You must rest a while before dinner this evening with the Comrade Secretary-General of the

Party's Provincial Branch. I will take you to the Love-the-Masses Hotel, where I have reserved a room for you."

Despite his dubious origins, Comrade N'g was a competent agitator. He knew all the manuals by heart. He had carefully studied Lenin's pamphlet *A Single Spark Can Start A Prairie Fire*. Which does not alter the fact that had he been less interested in westerns and more in the racing columns of Hong Kong, he would not be at work today laying tracks on the new China-Mongolia railroad somewhere between Kalgan and Ulan Bator.

He had chosen a Saturday for the D day of the great demonstration of the masses in Hong Kong. On that day, chanting "Long Live President Mao! Kill Truman!" an impressive delegation of the People's Red Cross moved toward the barricade in the middle of the Lowu Bridge that marks the frontier between the world of the Free Workers and the world of the enslaved. The delegation demanded free access to British territory in order to distribute the fruits of a collection spontaneously organized by the Chinese People on behalf of the victims of the criminal provocations of Chiang Kai-shek's henchmen, aided and abetted by imperialist accomplices.

"In the name of five hundred million Chinese, let us pass!"

On the other side of the barricade, a Chinese policeman represented Her Majesty. He had his instructions:

"Don't bother. Hand your contributions over to the Hong Kong Red Cross representatives, who will distribute them."

Comrade N'g had established his headquarters up close, in one of the frontier-police barracks.

"This was expected," he said to Comrade Chang Po-liang reassuringly. "Now we shall put the comrades in

Hong Kong to work. This barefaced rebuff of the colonialists will only serve to fan the just rancor of the masses."

He had, in fact, mobilized the Comrade activists on the other side. Upon telegraphic notice they formed a procession and set out through the streets of Kowloon in the direction of the border, a thousand strong.

The British police also had been mobilized. The riot squad had been trained all week on the handling of a rattan shield and a long bamboo truncheon.

Between these two forces, there was a clash. Blows were exchanged, several buses were overturned, a few windows broken.

"And the masses? Where are they?" worriedly inquired the Comrade Undersecretary of the Central Agitprop Bureau.

The masses were at the Happy Valley Hippodrome on the island of Hong Kong. The annual sweepstake had attracted all the racing fans of the Colony, that is to say, about 70 per cent of the Chinese population between twelve and seventy-five years of age. Marxism is powerless against a jackpot of nine hundred thousand Hong Kong dollars.

But the government officials of the Crown Colony had spent a nerve-racking quarter of an hour. And they were not at all anxious to repeat the experience.

II

"There are days when the Yellow River runs clear. May not man enjoy some happy hours?"

—CHINESE PROVERB

Mr. Pang was still in a bad humor when he came out of his shack. Night had not served to assuage his bitterness. Nor was there any comfort in the drizzling rain that was drenching Diamond Hill, although it meant at least that the shanty-town area would not catch fire. Mr. Pang padlocked the door, pulled his trousers up over his ankles, opened his oiled-paper umbrella, which stank of fish glue, and set out, as usual, to work.

Old Mr. Liao, who lived next-door at No. 17 and raised quails for their eggs (50 cents a dozen wholesale, 60 retail), was clamberng up the muddy path supporting a bamboo pole with bundles at each end. The path—like every other square inch of Hong Kong—was crowded, and when Mr. Liao called out, as he did at intervals, "Lend me your light!" the passers-by stepped aside.

Mr. Pang, absorbed in his somber thoughts, failed to see or hear and bumped into him. Mr. Liao lost his footing and collapsed into a puddle several feet farther down the hill, but not too far for him to hear Mr. Pang mutter: "You turtle egg, you!"

In the Middle Kingdom the turtle is sacred. Like Atlas it holds up the world, and at the same time symbolizes it, with its rounded shell, like the sky, and its square belly, like the earth below. It has the further merit, among others, of symbolizing long life and hence is quite naturally found in sculptured form, with a slender column above it, as a monument to the illustrious dead who have gone to life everlasting. But turtle eggs have no part in this glory. Once they have been laid their mother heedlessly abandons them. If you are a turtle egg there's no telling from whom you descend. And what is a man who cannot identify his ancestors? Less than the dust.

For these religious and zoological reasons, *Wang pa tang*, or "turtle egg," is the worst insult in the Chinese vocabulary, far worse than "pus bag" or "mixed mongrel species" or "two-hundred-and-fifty," that other subtle and mysterious appellation of a pungency all its own. To call someone "turtle egg" is to turn an argument into an exchange of blows.

Mr. Liao leaped to his feet, tore the stoutest branch off one of the logs, and charged at his adversary. Mr. Pang dodged the first blow, by sheer instinct, since he was still distracted, but the second shook him out of his daydreaming because his umbrella failed to ward it off and it descended on his left shoulder.

"Aaahhh! Are you crazy?"

Already some would-be mediators had stepped in.

"Me?" exclaimed Mr. Liao. "You bump into me and insult me to boot and then instead of apologizing you call me crazy? Where are your respect for old age and the eight virtues of those who have gone before us?"

"What do you mean, I insulted you?"

"You called me a turtle egg. There are plenty of people who heard you."

Mr. Liao looked around him for support, but the bystanders were unwilling to stick their necks out at this delicate stage of the negotiations.

"I called you a turtle egg?" said Mr. Pang, seeming to search his memory. "Yes, yes, you're quite right; I did say 'turtle egg,' but I wasn't talking to you because I didn't even see you. It's most embarrassing, Mr. Liao; I beg you to excuse me."

"And to whom *were* you talking?"

"I was thinking of those fellows down there," said Mr. Pang, pointing in a northerly direction, toward the far side of the mist-enshrouded Diamond Hill.

"What have they done now?"

Mr. Pang crouched down in the middle of the path and beckoned to Mr. Liao to do likewise, sheltering him under what was left of his umbrella. The numerous witnesses crouched around them, with the assistant detective Ch'en of the Secret Police in the front row.

"You know that when I came here from Shantung six months ago I left my family behind me . . ."

Mr. Liao and several of the witnesses nodded, and Mr. Pang went on:

"About a month ago, just after New Year's Day,* I had a letter from my wife's first cousin, saying that my wife was very ill. By the first mail I sent her some penicillin."

There was a hum of approval.

"Good stuff, penicillin; nothing better."

"Thanks to this medicine Mrs. Pang must have recovered her good health," put in Mr. Liao.

"No. She's dead. The penicillin never got there and she died of a raging fever."

"Terrible! Your sorrow is beyond endurance."

"Wait; that's not all. Since I have a job I asked my wife's cousin to send me the children. And do you know what she replied? That it's quite impossible. That they'd risk being corrupted by capitalism. They both belong to the Mao Tse-tung pioneers."

"Heaven and earth are silent!"

"But there's something more. I took out a loan of six hundred dollars, guaranteed by Mr. Kao, the relative for whom I'm working, and I sent a money order to the cousin for my wife's coffin and funeral expenses."

"You did right, Mr. Pang."

"Yesterday I had another letter from the cousin. It seems that funerals have been democratized and this one

* The Chinese New Year, in February.

cost only sixty-three dollars. The rest of the money was put into government bonds, to finance resistance to American imperialism and aid to North Korea. The cousin thanked me in the name of the Party. Those turtle eggs!"

"What else can you call them? Life's sheer misery for poor people like ourselves. One grief after another."

Mr. Pang got up, helped Mr. Liao to grapple his load, thanked his hearers for their sympathy, and went on his way. At the bottom of the hill Mrs. Hu, the soup-maker, hailed him.

"Mr. Pang, I have some good soya jelly with almonds today. Fifteen cents a bowl."

"Thank you, Mrs. Hu; I'm not hungry this morning."

Actually he was hungry, but with a debt of six hundred dollars at an interest of 10 per cent a month this was no time to waste money. Mr. Kao and his friends had been generous at that, because the regular interest was 20 per cent. If he saved enough he would be free of his debt by New Year's Day of the following year.

Quickening his step, with his knees bent forward and his feet dragging behind, Mr. Pang started down the tarred road along the northern edge of the Kaytak airfield. Beyond the gate some twenty freight carriers, disputed between Peking, Formosa and their American builders, were rusting on the grass beside the airstrip. On their rudders were the faded white sun disks of the Kuomintang, emblems of the Republic of China.

The Kuomintang . . . Mr. Pang was reminded of the happy days at Tsingtao, where he had worked as a waiter in an American Navy mess hall. Good pay and no worries. His wife and children had the clothes they needed, there were plenty of cigarettes, and he had bought both a bicycle and a camera. Every now and then there was a chance of selling a case of fruit juice or coffee. The Americans were rich and wasteful; an ordinary sailor made more than a Chinese general. Not bad fellows at all, those Americans. A bit noisy and excitable, that was all you could say against them. And he had picked up their language in the bargain.

But those days were gone forever. The liberators had come, and the Amercians had gone aboard their ships and planes just before their arrival, leaving an incredible number of radios, record players, clothes, books, canned goods, blankets, sheets and pieces of furniture behind them. There were even abandoned cars, but Mr. Pang hadn't dared lay hands on one of these because it would have made him too conspicuous.

The first days of the liberation had been a honeymoon. It was "the hundred old names"* here and "the hundred old names" there; they were always mouthing that magic phrase. The tightening-up process had been so gradual that Mr. Pang couldn't remember exactly how it began. But soon enough it became tiresome, then painful and finally dangerous, until the day when, at a neighborhood meeting, he found himself branded as a "tool of the imperialists," just because he had worked for the Americans. He made an immediate act of self-criticism, but it was judged inadequate. How then, he asked, was he to prove the sincerity of his progressive views? "By volunteering for Korea, comrade!"

That evening Mr. Pang dug up his little cache of dollars and silver money. The next day he waited until after the

* "The hundred old names" means "the people." There are no more than a hundred family names in all China, hence millions are named Wang, Li, Lü, Liu, Ch'en, Ma and hundreds of thousands Nieh, Mao, Liao and so on.

children had gone off to school; you never could tell what they might repeat outside. Then he kissed his wife goodbye. She understood at once but held back her tears for fear of the neighbors.

Going away was easy enough, but getting anywhere was a different matter. To cross China from north to south in 1951, the year of the great witch-hunt, was no joke. To go through a dozen roadblocks every day, showing his papers to suspicious militiamen and telling them his life story, then to go through it again with the security police at the entrance and exit of every town and with the innkeepers, to wait for hours at the station house for an answer to a telegraphic inquiry sent to the police headquarters of Tsingtao, and above all to conceal his precious money when he was searched from head to toe.

Mr. Pang smiled to himself when he remembered the ingenious solution he had found to all his troubles. It was so very simple that all those pumpkin heads had been taken in completely. That was his little secret and he would never give it away. A sudden access of good humor caused him to jump onto the bus at the corner of Nathan Road instead of walking for another half hour through Kowloon.

Only once in the course of his escape had he found himself in a tight spot. It was one night, when he was near the end of his journey. Only a few more yards to go, a stream to cross, a barbed-wire fence to cut through, and he would be in British territory. It was at this point that the "patriotic" smugglers of the Yellow Ox gang had done him out of his money.

"But we agreed on fifty American dollars."

"Yes. Only tonight there are two extra Communist sentries on duty."

He had no way of knowing if this was true. He had offered thirty dollars more.

"No, everything you've got."

"Ten pieces of silver."

"Everything on you, or we're not budging."

There was no way of arguing with them, and he arrived at Hong Kong with only two dollars in his pocket.

This memory made him regret having spent ten cents for the bus. He should have continued on foot; after all it wasn't raining so hard. He got off at the end of the line, at the southernmost extremity of Kowloon, and took the Star Ferry, second class, on the machine deck, with the coolies, standing up all the way in order not to dirty the trousers that he had so carefully cleaned and pressed with a bottle of hot water the night before.

Hong Kong had been good to him. He had run into Mr. Kao, the father-in-law of his wife's cousin, who was head-waiter at the Seaview Hotel and who took him on as his assistant. A stroke of real luck.

Getting off the ferry on the island of Hong Kong, he made his way to the quay, fraying a passage between piles of cabbages, cases of smoked fish, and chicken cages. Already the hotel was in view. The restaurant was famed for its genuine Tientsin cooking, and it was always crowded with bankers and shopkeepers from the north. Business was flourishing, in token of which Mr. Wu, the proprietor, had invested 1500 Hong Kong dollars in a blue neon sign, with English and Chinese letters, that could be seen at night all the way from Kowloon, on the other side of the harbor. On good days Mr. Pang took in six dollars in tips.*

He walked up the stairs. The restaurant was still empty;

* At this time six Hong Kong dollars equaled one United States dollar.

doubtless Mr. Wu had gone to the market. So much the better. He went into the kitchen and greeted the chef, Mr. Ma, who responded jovially to his salutation. That was a good sign; it meant that in answer to a tactful request he would serve the new arrival a bowl of noodles. Breakfast was always the hardest meal to arrange. For lunch and supper plenty of scraps were available.

Mr. Pang slipped off his dark jacket, tied an apron around his waist, and picked up a dish towel.

III

"In safety, be mindful of danger; In time of peace do not forget the possibility of revolution."

—CHINESE PROVERB

The regular Wednesday meeting with the Governor finished late, as usual. And, as usual, it was the fault of Peterson, who like all economists was a non-stop talker. "A thorny situation . . . an embargo . . . excess reserves of capital . . . speculation . . . recession . . ." There was no way of following him, or of cutting him short either. The Governor was entirely too patient.

Leslie Barrington-Jones' meditations were interrupted by the abrupt turn the car made at the entrance to Government House.

"We'll be off again in a couple of minutes," he said to the chauffeur.

He jumped out of the Humber and disdaining the snail-like elevator, which must have dated from the early widowhood of Queen Victoria, bounded, in spite of the heat, up the stairs to his third-floor office. Mechanically switching on the ceiling fan, he called out to his secretary:

"Phyllis, call the Dutch consul, will you, and ask him to forgive me if I'm late for lunch."

"Very good, sir. The N.O.C. called you twice this morning and asked you to call him back as soon as you came in."

"What can he want? I expect he's going to complain because a French admiral is coming in from Saigon Saturday or Sunday, just in time to ruin his game of golf."

"Not this time, sir. It's just the arrival of some foreign ships."

There has been a mistaken tendency in recent years to think of Great Britain as having fallen on evil days, as struggling in vain to breast the current of the mainstream of history. There is a simple test that proves the contrary to be true. What country leads all the rest by twenty years in its use of abbreviations? Spend the evening with an Englishman in a Hong Kong bar. You say: "Boy, bring me a gin and tonic;" he will say: "Boy, a G.T." By two o'clock in the morning he will be at least four glasses up on you.

For the benefit of the uninformed, the "N.O.C." (six-tenths of a second, even with an Oxford accent) is the Naval Officer Commanding (one and six-tenths seconds), and at Hong Kong in the year of grace 1952 this was Commodore Sir Bernard Leighton-Parker, K.C.B., known to his friends as Bobo.

"Call the consul first," said Leslie. "Then get me the N.O.C."

He had put his papers into his safe and was wiping the perspiration from his forehead when the telephone rang.

"Diplomatic adviser," he answered.

"Leslie," said the commodore's voice, "you've met Dick Blair, haven't you? He dropped in to ask for a stopover permit for two ships of the Seventh Fleet."

"Routine, isn't it, Bobo?"

"Not quite, or I shouldn't have rung you. The ships are an aircraft carrier and its escort."

"An aircraft carrier, no less!"

"Yes Sir."

"Those Americans are quite mad! I've always heard so, but I never believed it. An aircraft carrier—imagine! When one or two of the Formosa Patrol destroyers slip in without any fanfare, there's no objection. When they insisted on parking a transport, we didn't make any fuss, and the evacuation of American civilians couldn't be objected to. But an aircraft carrier! I thought you'd made it clear that we didn't want any of their big ships around as long as the war was on in Korea. Our relations with the Reds are shaky enough without their complicating them further. What did Blair say was the purpose of this friendly call?"

"Brace yourself, my boy! The purpose is recreation!"

"Recreation? My God! Haven't they enough recreation in Japan? It's absurd. How many sailors will there be?"

"The crews must be at full strength. That would mean between 2500 and 3000 between the two of them."

"It's madness, I tell you, Bobo! Can you imagine 3000 American sailors loose in Hong Kong and full of beans?"

"Beans?"

"You know perfectly well what I mean. But let's call it money. Do they think we can have a sweepstake every day?"

"Well, the sweepstake wasn't a bad idea, you must admit it."

"Stop joking, Bobo, this is serious. Listen to me now, I've been out here only four months, but any child can see what will happen. Peking will raise a stink. Indignant protests, demonstrations in front of our embassy, mass meetings all over China. You know the ploy, and there's no way of stopping it. Here in Hong Kong the *Ta Kung Pao* and other Party sheets will incite to murder. You'll see the headlines they'll come out with at the least run-in between a sailor and one of the Chinese. 'Criminal imperialist aggression,' 'An insult to the Chinese people,' and so on and so on. And if there isn't any incident you can be sure they'll provoke one."

"I'm with you, Leslie, believe me. But I'm up against having to give Dick Blair a yes or no answer. And if it's no, I'm counting on you to make it diplomatic. H. E. will have to have a cold or something of the sort, and it will be your business to speak for him."

"When do you have to let Blair know?"

"Just let me think. Today is April second, and the visit is planned for the twelfth to the sixteenth. The carrier is off the coast of Korea. Let's allow three days for getting here, two days for lying offshore, one day for an exchange of messages. You have three or four days to make up your mind."

"That's a tight squeeze. Of course I'll speak to H. E. just as soon as his A.D.C.* can make an appointment for me. But I'm sure the question will be referred to London. Wait a sec, though . . . there's one thing occurs to me . . . If we should say yes—mind, that's just a hypothesis—couldn't the men wear civvies when they come off the ships?"

"Not a chance! We'd better say no than depend on that. If necessary we can impose such a condition on our own men, but on the commander of a ship belonging to one of our allies, never."

This point calls for an explanation. When the People's Army of Liberation swept through southern China in 1949 the British saw fit to reinforce their Hong Kong garrison. An army division was assembled from the four corners of the Empire and Commonwealth and encamped near the Chinese border, in the mainland section of the Crown Colony north of Kowloon, which has been called since the beginning of the last century the "New Territories." In the division was a large proportion of hard-bitten veterans, very well disciplined when on duty but somewhat rowdy after five in the afternoon and over the weekend. Inevitably there were misunderstandings between the mixed Scots, Irishmen and Englishmen on the one side and the Chinese on the other. The Chinese press, with one accord, made a patriotic protest. But fortunately His Majesty's administration had some brains in its service. One of

* Aide-de-camp.

them cooked up the idea that the troops should wear civilian clothes whenever they were away from the encampment. Of course the soldiers were still recognizable in their single disguise–sport shirt, cotton slacks and tennis shoes—and with their pink-cheeked white faces. But if any of them got involved in a scrap the duly-coached conservative press simply referred to him as a "European." Only when some run-in involved a Swede, a Belgian, a Greek or a Venezuelan was there any mention of nationality.

"Bobo, I must be off to lunch. I'll try to get to H. E. as soon as possible. But don't be impatient; the matter's too hot for us to handle on the spot."

"O.K. Shall I see you this evening at the Portuguese cocktail party?"

"Absolutely. Goodbye."

His Excellency listened without interrupting the report of his diplomatic adviser. Then, letting his eyes wander over the teak panels on his office walls and contemplating the picture of the Queen, he said:

"No objection."

A public school education and diplomatic training have their good points. In spite of his surprise Leslie was silent for no more than three seconds.

"Very well, Your Excellency."

The Governor must have his reasons. And he was the chief.

"By the way, Leslie," he mumbled as his adviser was going out the door, "better have a word with the Honorable Secretary and the Chief of Police, so that they can make the proper arrangements."

That evening Phyllis's roommates noticed that she was in a state of excitement. But she knew how to hold her tongue where office affairs were concerned and they couldn't get her to explain. The next day she had the hairdresser give her a permanent wave.

IV

"Even if the lamb is succulent, it isn't easy to please all the guests."

—CHINESE PROVERB

On April 12, 1952, the U.S.S. *Bull Run,* commonly known as "Big Bully" (displacement 31,000 tons, 2100 officers and men), followed by the destroyer *MacBain,* sailed through the narrow strait of Lei Yue Mun and majestically entered Victoria Harbor. The armada of junks in the channel prudently made way, and the carrier anchored a few cable lengths from the Royal Hong Kong Yacht Club, in front of tiny Kellett Island.

At the landing of the Royal Dockyard the ladies of the American Club, led by the Reverend Patrick O'Hara, were busily heating coffee and setting out cakes on improvised trestles. Twelve buses, rented by the naval attaché, were drawn up in the roadway waiting to take sailors on a conducted tour of the island. The *Bull Run*'s arrival had been kept secret, and for this reason no more than five or six hundred Chinese guides were huddled outside the gate.

The boats started coming in about eleven o'clock, and the first sailors leaped onto the landing, with cameras slung over their shoulders and a gleam in their eyes, obviously eager to conquer the Crown Colony. But it was favorably noted that they tempered their haste long enough to tell the American Club ladies how grateful they were for their attentions. Noted also was the fact that several of the buses went away empty.

Four days later the *Bull Run* set sail again, with its faithful escort trailing close behind. Contrary to expectations nothing untoward had happened. Peking had chosen to overlook the incident, the *Ta Kung Pao* had remained silent and there had been no provocation to trouble. As for the sailors, they had behaved like gentlemen at one of Edward VII's garden parties at Balmoral. This was a minor miracle, when one stops to think of the rigid prohibition of alcohol enforced by the United States Navy and of the variety and cheapness of the whiskies, gins, brandies, rums, vodkas and other strong medicines stacked all the way to the ceiling in the Hong Kong bars.

There was only one thing. No sooner had the wake of the aircraft carrier disappeared from the green waters of the mouth of the River of Pearls than the English-language daily, the *Hong Kong Chronicle,* came out with an inconspicuous item that read:

> AN AVALANCHE OF GREENBACKS DESCENDS UPON HONG KONG
>
> According to a conservative estimate, the *Bull Run's* visit yielded our colony a million American dollars.

Only a few Hong Kong Chinese can read English. But the others needed no newspaper to inform them of the beneficent effects of the American visit. The general effect was as overwhelming, in a far more pleasant way, as that produced by Typhoon "Sarah," whose tail had lashed the Crown Colony the preceding autumn, flooding the low-lying sections of the city, sinking junks, destroying squatters' shacks and uprooting kapok trees.

The sailors had descended on the shops of Hong Kong and Kowloon like a cloud of locusts arriving from the Sudan desert at the delta of the Nile. Tweed suits made to order in twenty-four hours, silk kimonos and pajamas with embroidered dragons, brocaded jackets, carved camphorwood boxes, nested ivory balls, jade and crystal statuettes, cloisonné enamels, Japanese cameras and cultured pearls (even cheaper than in Japan) were swept away at the asking price, without discussion. For indefinable but doubtless unscientific reasons some of the visitors had nearly bought out an old-fashioned Chinese pharmacy, one that sold mysterious herbal teas, snake-bile tonic and rare dried mushrooms grown out of a drop of tiger's milk or in the interior of a coffin, on the exact spot where the dead man had exhaled his last breath.

Old China hands say that a Chinese shopkeeper likes nothing better than a round of bargaining. This is why his initial price is so outrageous and why it is positively cruel to deprive him of the joy of making a good deal, once he has guessed at the wealth and bargaining ability of his customer. If one pays the ten dollars he asks for a package of cigarettes that can be had almost anywhere for one, he will be desolate because it shows that he could just as well have asked fifteen or twenty.

The *Bull Run* episode proves the complete error of this reactionary theory. The American sailors' direct approach—"How much? . . . I'll take it"—caused no frustration, much less neurosis, among the Chinese shopkeepers. When Dr. Hyde, the psychiatrist of the King George Hospital, was questioned on this score at the Hong Kong Club, he stated that the number of patients admitted to his service was 34 per cent less than usual. Indeed, there had been some cures that some of his colleagues branded as miraculous but that he did not hesitate to attribute to the therapeutic power of the American dollar. Similar cures had been observed in both the general and the surgical wards.

The manna did not fall on shopkeepers alone. Guides from the Tiger-Balm Gardens appeared at stockbrokers' offices. Three rickshaw men from the station near the Peninsula Hotel were reliably reported to have sold the vehicles that had formerly afforded them a livelihood. One had opened a pawnshop, another an import-export house and the third had set up a toothbrush factory where he had already taken on eight employees.

Bobo was not surprised when Leslie telephoned him one morning toward the end of April.

"Look here, old chap, next time you see Dick Blair, tell him that if any more U. S. ships want to put in at Hong Kong they'll be welcome. The bigger the better, in fact the entire Seventh Fleet, if it wants to come."

The crew of the *Bull Run* did not entirely share the enthusiasm of the government and population of the Crown Colony. The day before arrival, when the carrier was sailing southward along the east coast of Formosa, a squad of mechanics was going over the cooling system of a Corsair that had caused considerable worry to its pilot. Zilling, a petty officer better known as "Daddy" because he had been called up from the reserves for the Korean war, was inspecting their work when the loudspeakers boomed out:

"Now hear this. Now hear this."

All hands were silent.

"Our destination is Hong Kong. Our E.T.A. is 0900 hours tomorrow."

"That's real hot poop!" exclaimed Daddy.

"What's so hot about it?" asked Simpson, commonly called "Pimples."

"Hong Kong's in China."

"So what?"

"So the women are Chinese."

"What's special about them?"

"If you don't find out it'll mean you're still a virgin."

"No kidding, Daddy, are they so good in the sack?"

"Good! Boy, once you've had a Chinese woman you won't want no other kind."

"How come?"

"Because they're different."

"Hotter?"

"No, different."

"What have they got that the Japs haven't got?"

"Nothing. They're just different in the right place."

"You mean something like slanted eyes?"

"You'll see for yourself. Let's get going with this job. Did you change the oil valve?"

Zilling was known to have served with the Flying Tigers during the Second World War, so he could be credited with first-hand knowledge of Chinese women. Half an hour later his words of wisdom had made the rounds of the *Bull Run* and traveled to the machine room of the *MacBain.*

"You know what? Chinese women have it crosswise instead of up and down."

"Sure! Like your sister!"

"It's official, you dope! Straight from the Big Bully!"

There is no place like Hong Kong for sheer beauty. One can live there for years without tiring of the landscape. As for prices, they are so low that residents and visitors alike ruin themselves with bargains.

But when it came to real fun, at least at the time of this moral fable, Hong Kong was dead as a doornail. And real fun was uppermost in the minds of the well-fed, virile young sailors who had spent several uninterrupted months on maneuvers in the vicinity of the 38th parallel, with nothing but pin-up girls to cheer them. After all, they had opted for the Navy in the first place because they'd been promised a girl in every port.

But Hong Kong, as we have said, had none of the attractions of Shanghai before Mao Tse-tung, of post-Tojo Tokyo or even of Murmansk after de-Stalinization. There were a few night clubs, but they were models of dullness.

At midnight sharp the band struck up "God Save the Queen" and "Goodnight, Ladies." When the famous taxi girls of Shanghai fled from Karl Marx and social re-education, they took one look at Hong Kong and went on to Hanoi, Bangkok and Manila.

One or two or even ten sailors could, with considerable effort, find the diversion they sought. But not three thousand, especially if the Honorable Secretary and the Chief of Police had had time to arrange things beforehand. First, there was the famous Anglo-Saxon puritan spirit. In England customs may have relaxed, but the Empire, and after it the Commonwealth, have not kept step with the times. There is always the fear of creating a scandal in front of or, for that matter, with the natives. In the second place, Her Majesty's government in Hong Kong did not relish being accused by the powerful and all-too-near Communists of favoring debauchery among the working class in order to cater to the vices of the bourgeois imperialists, who are corrupt by definition.

So one-night stands were discouraged. Ladies of great heart and small virtue were invited to leave the streets; hotels were closely watched and shut down for the least infraction of the law. Stubborn pursuers of exotic and erotic delights were advised to look for them in Macao. But Macao was barred to the Americans by the fact that there were Chinese territorial waters in the way.

Disappointment aboard the *Bull Run* was as great as the sailors' expectant appetite—which is saying plenty. The few lucky ones who had hit the jackpot vehemently denied, on the basis of their experience, the legend about Chinese female anatomy. But nobody believed them—a bunch of braggarts. Their "experience"? Phooie!

V

"Stop to think three times before you act:
You might do well to think even longer."

—CHINESE PROVERB

Another disappointed man was Mr. Wu, the proprietor of the Seaview Hotel, who was talking over the situation with Mr. Kao, the headwaiter. How had it happened that, in spite of the new, fifteen-hundred-dollar neon sign, not a single American sailor had turned up at the restaurant? It was all very odd. Mr. Kao suggested consulting Mr. Pang, his assistant, who had a first-hand acquaintance with Americans.

"I'm not surprised," said Mr. Pang. "They're not allowed to go any place that hasn't official approval."

Mr. Wu was impressed by his employee's insight.

"Couldn't we get ourselves approved? After all, we have the best Tientsin cooking in the city. Our chicken and peppers, our fish-head soup, our steamed eel, our pancakes with scallions, our ravioli and noodles, our light precious pudding . . ."

He seemed to have embarked on a recital of the whole bill of fare, on which there were a hundred and twenty-three soups just to begin with. But Mr. Pang cut him short.

"It's not a matter of the cooking, Mr. Wu. What the Americans care about is cleanliness. They're afraid of catching something."

"There's no cleaner kitchen in all Hong Kong. They're welcome to come and inspect it. Doesn't Mr. Ma wash his hands every morning?"

"Of course, but that's not enough. You have to know someone inside the American naval attaché's office . . . the interpreter or the chauffeur. Only that would cost money. All the fellows there are from Shanghai, and you know what that means."

"How much would it come to?"

"It all depends . . ."

Mr. Pang went on. A restaurant, he pointed out, was not

really the best means of attracting the American sailors' money. They had no appreciation of Chinese cooking; in fact, they mistrusted it. The stuff that was dished out to them under his name in the mess hall at Tsingtao . . . Chef Ma Pang would rather give up his job than serve it. Things they called chop suey, egg fu yung, chow mein . . . No, the big money was in something quite different . . .

"For instance?"

Well, the other day, on the Star Ferry, Mr. Pang had met, quite by chance, young Lin Tse-tan, whose father had a motion-picture theater at Tsingtao . . .

"And one at Kunming, during the war?"

Exactly. Young Lin had just come back from a business trip to Japan. There he had found out that the Japanese were cashing in on a new kind of theater, something called *Sse-tu-li-pu-ti-sze*. Nothing so very wonderful, quite stupid, in fact, Lin had told him . . . just a bunch of girls taking off their clothes, one after the other.

"In front of the audience?"

Precisely, Mr. Pang assured him. Foreign devils, and particularly American sailors, found this kind of show enchanting, and the theaters were going full blast. Lin was thinking of opening up something of the sort at Hong Kong, but he needed 25,000 dollars to start it and all he had was 5000. If Mr. Wu could borrow some money from the Sons of Shantung, of which he was the honorable vice-president, it would be a first-class investment. Even at 20 per cent interest the loan would be repaid within a few months; he could count on it, and after that it would be all gravy. Lin was young, of course, but highly reliable. If Mr. Wu wanted, he himself, Mr. Pang, would be glad to serve as technical director and watch out for his employer's interests.

The new theater, the Lido, opened its doors on June 2, 1952. The opening coincided—and not by accident, since the interior still smelled of wet plaster—with the arrival (secret, of course) of the U.S.S. *Java Sea* (31,000 tons and a crew of 2100), which like the *Bull Run* had put in, with its escort, for purposes of well-deserved recreation.

The theater was on a street parallel to the waterfront, not far from the entrance to the naval base, in the heavily populated Chinese quarter of Wanchai. Only four days before, the site had been occupied by a warehouse, and there were still pulley blocks and big hooks on the little balcony erected for the orchestra. Another balcony in the rear, also festooned with pulleys, was set aside for the electricians and their battery of spotlights. The stage, a rectangular platform swathed in black velvet, was in the middle of the room, with benches and chairs all around it except for a narrow passageway for the performers.

The gala opening was a huge success, both from an artistic and a financial point of view. Mr. Pang had alerted the taxi drivers, promising them twenty-five cents for every passenger they brought in, recruited a corps of guides, and arranged for reciprocal publicity with the local tailors—by appointment purveyors to the democratic U. S. Navy. He himself had gotten up the program, whose star attraction was Miss Orchid of Chiu Li Tsun (Szechwan).

Under a yellow (the imperial color) spotlight Miss Orchid made her way, with difficulty, to the stage. Mr. Lin at once suggested to Mr. Pang that the passageway must be widened so as to safeguard the performers from the sailors' eager hands. Mr. Pang counterproposed that the seats adjacent to the aisle be higher priced than the rest, a suggestion that won him immediate favor in the eyes of his backer, Mr. Wu.

The orchestra on the balcony, which had so far played only fox trots and waltzes, broke into a medley of Chinese airs from the celebrated opera *The Imperial Concubine,* sung by a falsetto voice to the accompaniment of two-string violins and occasional bamboo castanets and gongs, the latter sounding at completely random intervals.

Miss Orchid clambered, somewhat awkwardly, up onto the stage. She was wearing her hair in Joan-of-Arc style and was covered by a padded blue cotton Chinese peasant jacket and trousers. Without raising her eyes from the floor she divested herself of these and appeared in a plain gray dress. Underneath this was a sheath of sumptuous purple brocade, slashed at either side up to the hip. The sight of her superb legs roused a storm of whistles and catcalls so loud the orchestra was drowned out, perhaps fortunately, as the unpracticed male singer was mingling baritone notes with his shrill falsetto.

When she was at last revealed in her full natural glory a complete silence, cut by a single "Geez!", descended on the half of the audience that had a front view. Miss Orchid was flat, absolutely flat, a classic Chinese doll, except for her normal feet, one of the race of beauties that had caused the thrones of the Soong and Ming and Ching emperors to tremble, a creature as slender as a boy, but with a difference.

The other half of the audience, wondering what was on the opposite side of the moon, began to stamp and to call out in chorus: "Turn around! Turn around!" Mr. Pang leaped up onto the stage and made her do an about-face, leaving her new admirers speechless, while the former ones exchanged incredulous murmurs. Some of the sailors, armed with flashbulbs and light-meters, focused their cameras on her. Here was proof that Chinese women were, indeed, like no others.

Mr. Pang had arrived at Art; what he got was P. T. Barnum. But what did it matter, as long as the customers were pleased? In all justice to Mr. Pang, he had been acquainted, all along, with the American idea of beauty, as exemplified in the pin-up girl, drawing his knowledge from the *Esquire's* and other magazines strewn about the mess hall at Tsingtao, which he had zealously studied before reselling them on the local market. The Misses Opalescent Moon of Soochow, Springtime Harmony of Taiyuan, and Pine Balm of Ningpo, to mention only a few of the reigning ersatz-American beauties, were no less shapely than Jayne Mansfield.

Mr. Wu was beaming as he helped the cashier stack up the dollar bills in piles, first of tens and then of hundreds.

VI

"If fire devours the gates of the
city
The damage will spread to the
fish in the lake."

—CHINESE PROVERB

It would be wrong, and unjust as well, to suppose that the Hong Kong police did not know what was going on at the Lido. The Crown Colony's police force was, and presumably still is, quite able to cope with any situation. In this instance, the situation, quite out of the ordinary, was matched by the police force's efficiency.

Since Mao Tse-tung's assumption of power in China the population of Hong Kong had tripled. The limited area of the Crown Colony, so arid that water had to be rationed, had taken in two million poverty-stricken refugees and exposed them to an atmosphere of extreme prosperity, to shop windows overflowing with luxury products from all over the globe. Because the refugees included a normal percentage of criminals, whose records the Mao Tse-tung government had no intention of transmitting, there was every reason to expect a sharp increase of crime. And yet very little trouble had ensued. The threat of expulsion to the Marxist paradise was a strong deterrent. There were few burglaries and hold-ups, and almost no murders. Usually the police were alerted in advance and asked to prevent them. When they occurred without warning, the guilty parties were almost invariably arrested within a week's time.

A miracle? No, simply the first-class job of a nucleus of highly competent British inspectors in charge of an elite corps of well-trained Chinese policemen who were assisted, in turn, by a swarm of more or less disinterested informers. Some people went so far as to say that one out of every two Chinese was an informer. Making due allowance for exaggeration, let us say the percentage was one out of three.

Mr. Kao himself, the headwaiter at the Seaview Hotel, father-in-law of Mr. Pang's wife's cousin, had revealed the project of a strip-tease theater when it was still in the preliminary stages. The news had traveled from second-class detective Liu to detective Kuo, to Inspector MacIntosh, to Chief-Inspector Graham, to Commissioner Brown, to the Police Superintendent, to H. S. (the Honorable Secretary) and finally to H. E. (the Governor) in person.

A summit meeting was called to order. The first question was this: was it necessary or advisable, for the sake of law and order in the Crown Colony, to block the establishment of a vaudeville theater intended to provide amusement for the United States Navy? And the majority answer was no. It would have been positively inhuman to deprive the American sailors of this diversion. Every day on the streets they were bombarded by the sight of Chinese girls whose slashed skirts innocently revealed their legs almost up to the hips. To oppose the theater was asking for trouble.

A small conservative minority voiced doubts as to the efficacy of the diversion. A strip-tease theater would only fan the flames. Strict logic demanded an even more drastic solution, such as that of wide-open Macao.

H. E. responded with a vague nod to both contentions, signifying merely that he had taken in the arguments on either side.

The second question was economic. What repercussions would a veto of the theater project have on local business? "Disastrous! . . . No, untoward." (The speaker had been carried away by his Irish blood.) The democratic ways of the Americans, which extended even to their Navy, had to be taken into account. If the sailors in search of recreation failed to find what they were looking for, it was likely that complaints would go to their congressmen, to the White

House, to the Pentagon, and back to CINCPAC, and finally the ships of the Seventh Fleet would no longer visit the Crown Colony. This meant the loss of two or three million American dollars a month. The long-winded Peterson was the one to develop this theory, but for once Leslie made an effort to listen. As for H. E., he nodded.

And what about the political effects of an economic setback? Dangerous, that was the only way to describe them. A recession was already present because of the embargo placed on the sale of military goods to China. Any aggravation would tend to produce a social upheaval that would play into the hands of local Communist agitators, who had been searching, so far unsuccessfully, for a lever with which to arouse the masses. Peterson pointed out that there were ten candidates for every vacant job, and this in the category of technically trained workers. Having a captive audience before him, he proceeded to enlarge on the benefits that two or three million American dollars would bring to the marketplace. ("Theorizing as usual," Leslie mumbled to himself, tapping a Capstan on his cigarette case.) These millions would make the rounds of the city, after which approximately 10 per cent would be withdrawn in one way or another from circulation, then make the rounds a second, third, fourth and fifth time, with proportionately diminishing returns. By means of a simple mathematical formula . . .

Leslie emerged from his daydreaming just in time for the next question, which interested him considerably more.

Would the government of the Democratic People's Republic of China react to the new theater, and if so, how? A reaction of some sort was to be expected, but a strictly formalistic one, since it would find no support among the local population. And there were various ways of countering Peking's propaganda. First, by limiting the number of theaters of this very special kind; second, by prohibiting any advertisement of their activities; third, by pretending to know nothing about them.

What, then, would be the government's policy? To ignore the Lido just as long as it gave no cause for scandal.

After the meeting Leslie went for a swim in the pool of the nearby Ladies' Recreation Club, where he had guest privileges. Observing the knee-length of the voluminous, killjoy shorts worn by the lady tennis players, he thanked heaven that their club was hidden from the street by a high hedge. If American sailors were to glimpse these examples of womanhood they might very possibly spend the remainder of their leave aboard ship. It must be said, in Leslie's defense, that he had never been posted to the United States, where the effect of Bermuda shorts is equally damping. His thoughts wandered to the Sport Club at Saigon, where he had made an all-too-short stopover.

The government congratulated itself on its wise decision when inspectors MacIntosh and Wilson, who had attended the opening performance disguised as sailors (they were in fact among the "eager hands" next to the performers' passageway), reported that it was "basically" a very innocent affair. Except for the noise, of which none of the theater's neighbors complained, everything went very well. The riot squad, which had been kept on the alert, had found no reason to intervene.

VII

"To build it up, a century was not sufficient;
To tear it down, a single day was too long."

—CHINESE PROVERB

The last storms of the monsoon period are often the most terrible. It had rained all night and Mr. Pang had spent endless hours trying to patch the leaks in his roof. His bed was soaking when he finally went back to sleep. But he was in a cheerful mood this morning. It was good weather, a little hot and humid perhaps. Carefully he padlocked the door of the shack, tucked his umbrella under his arm, and started out. The path was dusty again after the storm.

Outside number seventeen, Mr. Liao was cleaning his quail cages. He scraped the bottom to collect droppings in an old tin can. Gardening enthusiasts consider this the best fertilizer for chrysanthemums.

"A peaceful morning to you," said Mr. Pang.

"A peaceful morning," replied Mr. Liao. "How are the children?"

"Same story. I wrote again last month, but my wife's cousin doesn't want to send them to me. Look, Mr. Liao, here's a poem my oldest boy wrote for his pioneer group."

"Read it to me, Mr. Pang, I haven't got my glasses."

"I know it by heart—I'll recite it to you:

"'*The Cog*

A cog is humble and small.
In a machine numberless are the cogs, humble and small.
But without the cog, who could run the machine?

In the China of Mao Tse-tung
The activists are the cogs.
Who does not dream of being a cog for President Mao?'"

"That's marvelous, Mr. Pang! A son who is already a poet! A future Hanlin.*" Mr. Pang thanked him, sighed and moved on. Crossing the fourth block he shot a glance at Miss Orchid's alley. Her shack was closed—she wasn't up yet at this early hour.

Mr. Pang stopped at the foot of Diamond Hill at Mrs. Hu's. "They're piping hot, Mr. Pang, these little steamed buns stuffed with plums—only twelve cents."

Mr. Pang turned his pocket inside out, kept ten cents aside and counted the rest. "I've only got eight cents, Mrs. Hu; I need credit."

"Till New Year's, I suppose. And how am I going to live till then?"

Mr. Pang helped himself and munched on the hot bread. With his mouth full he said:

"If you'd marry me you wouldn't need to give me credit."

"May the rats get your liver, you cheeky devil," Mrs. Hu retorted, and pretending to be infuriated she started shooing him away.

He continued along the wide tar road. There was no hurry. He crossed the whole city of Kowloon on foot and took a second-class seat on the Star Ferry, as usual. On the other side of the harbor he latched onto the crowd clinging to the tramway's side and detached himself, having as usual paid nothing, in front of the Wanchai naval base. A few minutes later he walked into the Lido.

A team of coolies was sweeping the place. Mr. Pang went into the dressing room and called, "Ah Hing!" The young steward came running. "I want a hot tub." Mr. Pang took his clothes off, hung them on a hook, and gave himself a thorough washing. Then he took his electric razor out of a cabinet. It wasn't that he needed to shave,

* Hanlin: the top grade in the academic hierarchy of classical China.

since like most Chinese he had a light beard, but because he wanted to acquire status. For that reason he had bought the noisiest possible razor.

His wardrobe contained a collection of smartly tailored suits, a gift from the association of tailors accredited by the United States Navy. He chose a tan Palm Beach outfit with a yellow polka-dot tie over his heavily starched shirt front and a pair of white and tan shoes. With the two Parker pens showing in his vest pocket, he looked like a candidate for the Junior Chamber of Commerce.

"Mr. Hsieh is here," said Ah Hing.

"Coming."

Mr. Pang went into the theater manager's office adjoining the dressing room and took his wallet and his dark glasses from the safe. Now he was ready.

Mr. Hsieh, the driving instructor, came every morning at nine to give Mr. Pang his lesson. Mr. Pang had recently bought, for cash, a Morris Oxford painted a sober black. To be sure it was not new, but it was in very good condition. In six months, with a little luck, he could have his license. For Europeans the procedure was faster, but the Chinese had to wait their turn. The car was parked in front of the Lido. Ah Hing had taken the paint off with his conscientious polishing—he was already on his second duster. Mr. Pang himself put the required "Learner" signs on the bumpers and then took his place behind the wheel.

Start her, put out your right hand, in first, let in the clutch, go ahead slowly.

"Very good, Mr. Pang, you are my best student. You've stalled, there's nothing wrong with that, it's because of the taxi that cut in front of you. Repeat everything, from the beginning."

At ten-fifteen Mr. Pang received eight prospective performers in his office, two of whom were accompanied by their mothers. Or so they said.

"Please get undressed, young ladies."

"Completely?" demanded one mother.

"Naturally, madam."

Calmly he proceeded to light his pipe. He didn't really like to smoke, but he'd heard that all the impresarios in London did it. As it was warm and all the candidates were lightly clad they were quickly ready. Mr. Pang rapidly analyzed their charms and pointing his pipe in the direction of each girl in succession he gave out with a "No . . . No . . . Yes . . . No . . . No . . . No . . . No . . . No . . ."

"What do you mean, 'No'?" one virago shouted. "My daughter isn't beautiful enough for you? Let me tell you she has turned down six marriage proposals!"

"Understand, it's not a matter of my own taste, madam, or else your daughter would have received a seventh proposal by now! Look at this young lady's bosom, the one I have hired. That's the type my American clients go for."

"Goats' udders full of wind! That's the kind of tart they want, is it?"

Mr. Lin showed up just in time to help the technical director break it up between the goats' udders and the classic bosoms and throw everybody out.

"It's noon. Where are we eating lunch today?"

"How about the Seaview?"

Mr. Kao had reserved a table for three by the window, the choice spot from which you could see the stevedores working on the junks' docks. Mr. Pang respectfully greeted Mr. Wu, who was at the next table chummily bending over the banker Han, President of the Association of the Sons of Shantung.

"What's good today, Mr. Kao?"

"I suggest cold patty with mustard, eels in garlic, casserole of lion's head, little-dragon, and, lastly, silk-sugared apple."

"Excellent. With a pot of Shao Hsing, and make sure it's really hot. The real thing, not the stuff they make here."

"We got in ten jars yesterday, straight from the country. A wine like that isn't something we suggest to just anybody."

Mr. Lin and Mr. Pang nibbled watermelon seeds while waiting for the third member of their party, who was not long in joining them.

Mr. Lap, a Cantonese, was the nephew of the superintendent of the building where the American naval attaché had his offices. He was a son of a good family who might have been successful if he had been able to curb some of his interest in pleasure. As it was, he was something of a small-time gangster with an overdose of vanity.

During the casserole of lions' heads, Mr. Pang raised the serious subject:

"Well?"

"In six days a cruiser and two destroyers."

"Two thousand sailors?"

"More than that, it's the flagship. Crammed with staff people. Let's say two thousand two hundred or three hundred."

"Bad for business: a flagship always spends more time in port than at sea."

"Don't you believe it, Mr. Pang. The American sailors save their money for Hong Kong. My uncle heard a chauffeur of the naval attaché say that the Japanese government complained to MacArthur or his replacement."

"Okay, and what next?"

"Then there is a flotilla of frigates, eight or nine."

"When?"

"From the seventeenth to the twenty-second of October."

"That's all?"

"No, I saved the best for last: on the twenty-third of October, there's a group of transports, three ships, each with eleven hundred sailors on leave from Japan. What do you say to that?"

Mr. Pang handed Mr. Lap a hundred dollar bill under the table. They rinsed their mouths with a sip of tea, which they spat into the bowls provided for the purpose. Mr. Lap excused himself and left. Mr. Pang went over to the kitchen where he greeted Mr. Ma.

"How's business, Mr. Pang?"

"Tough. As the ancients said, 'Making money is like shoveling sand with a needle.'"

"'Money is spent like sand swept away by a flood.' Ah, yes!" said Mr. Ma. "If you would like a bowl of fresh noodles one of these mornings, feel free to come get them."

"Many thanks, Mr. Ma. Here's something for you."

"Two dollars? That's crazy, Mr. Pang!"

"It's for all the meals in the past."

People were leaving the restaurant by now and Mr. Kao was not so busy.

"Mr. Kao," said Mr. Pang, "this morning I figured out how much I owe the friends of yours who lent me six hundred dollars for my wife's burial. It comes to one thousand and twenty dollars. Here's a check."

"There wasn't any rush. Why not wait till New Year's?"

"It's already settled. Kindly convey my heartiest thanks to your friends."

It was two-thirty, and the first matinée performance

began at three. Mr. Pang and Mr. Lin took a taxi to the Lido. The house was already full. Mr. Pang crossed the room in great strides and went to change his clothes in the dressing room. In three minutes he was dressed in his dinner jacket.

"Hurry, Miss Springtime Harmony, you're on first today. And you, the new one there, get with it because you're on stage starting tonight!"

Mr. Pang found time between shows to draw up a bulletin forecasting American ship movements, which he immediately sent off with Ah Hing to Mr. Fu, of Yang & Co., Tailors, for general distribution to the tailors' association. Between shows he also studied the accounts of last night's performance with the cashier, Mr. Kwei, and took note of the important figures.

Between the third matinée, which was at seven o'clock, and the first evening show, which began an hour later, the Board of Directors of the Lido held a meeting in the Morris Oxford, where they were more or less safe from eavesdroppers.

Mr. Pang outlined the financial situation. On October 8 the establishment had assets of $55,384: $49,567 deposited at the Han Bank and $5,817 in the till.

The third of October had yielded $5200 in receipts, while expenses rose to $1903, making a gross profit of $3297. This statement was approved.

Next Mr. Pang outlined possibilities for the immediate future. In particular he stressed the imminent arrival of about four thousand sailors, transport crews and men on leave. He had a proposal to submit to the board on this point.

As everybody knew, his negotiations with Mr. Yip had

failed. Mr. Yip was the proprietor of the restaurant next door, which had the good fortune to hold a liquor license. The restaurant's profits had, at a conservative estimate, tripled since the Lido opened. It would have been per-only fair for Mr. Yip to give the Lido a percentage of his profit. To what did he owe his present profits if not to the sailors who crowded into his bar before and after the show? But he had refused. "Not a cent," he had flatly declared to Mr. Pang.

One ought not be surprised at anything coming from a Cantonese. If Mr. Yip had been brought up in Shantung among civilized people he would not even have had to be approached; he would have made the appropriate gesture on his own. But since he had proved to be so crude, perhaps the time had come to play another game.

"Like what?" Mr. Wu asked.

"We could rent the shoe shop next door. The owner won't ask much since his business isn't going well. We could turn it into a bar."

"And you think you can get a liquor license just like that? I put in for one for the Seaview eighteen months ago and I'm still waiting. For Chinese wine, fine, it comes right away. But for the foreigners' alcohols you can wait till rice grows out of the sea!"

"With all due respect, Mr. Wu, you may not have approached the right person."

"Go right ahead. But just watch out. This isn't Kuomintang China. Offer a policeman ten dollars and you may be deported."

"What about beer? The Americans drink a lot of that."

"Same as for alcohol, you've got to have a license."

"All right, so Coca-Cola and lemonade."

"If you want, but we're not going to make much selling lemonade. Not a bad idea, though."

"It's no use buying the store next door under these conditions," put in Mr. Lin. "We'll serve drinks in the theater."

"You'll have to be careful with the bottles," Mr. Pang warned. "They have to be collected as soon as they're empty. I saw a free-for-all once at Tsingtao between American soldiers and Marines. They broke up everything with their bottles: heads, windowpanes, doors . . ."

Mr. Wu inquired if a replacement had been found for Miss Pine Balm.

"This very morning," Mr. Pang replied. "A Miss Precious Treasure."

"Where's she from?"

"Hangchow. You'll see her in a minute."

"Let's hope she's not married."

"She says her husband's in Black Dragon province. Manchuria is several thousand *li** from Hong Kong."

"Pine Balm's husband was in Kansu, in the far west, but he still managed to join her and give her a baby."

So many sailors were crowding the door of the Lido for the second show, all protesting that they could not come back as their boat was sailing in the morning, that Mr. Pang took a good look at the two strapping brutes from the Shore Patrol and decided to put on a third show for six dollars a head instead of five. After all, the performers had to be recompensed for their extra effort.

The show went along as usual until Miss Orchid's number. She had just slipped out of her brocade sheath and

* About a quarter of a mile.

was showing her classical figure when a wild yell went up from the seats. A young, gangling sailor with a pimply face bounded up to the stage shaking off the buddies who were trying to stop him. He lunged after the terror-stricken Miss Orchid, threw away the cigar he had been chomping on, and snapped a close-up picture.

The two Shore Patrolmen rushed through the riotous audience and grabbed the offender, who moaned, "Just one more shot," and threw him out with a last whack from their truncheons for good measure. Outside, a jeep siren blasted as he was taken off to the police station. Miss Orchid quickly pulled herself together and got on with her number. Mr. Pang breathed a sigh of relief.

It was at this point that a sailor smelled something burning. He mentioned it to the fellow on his right, who started sniffing too. He had a cold and his vigorous sniffing could be heard above the sing-song emitted by the orchestra.

"Can't you blow your nose, you slob?"

"Can't you smell something burning?"

"Burning? What's burning?"

A trail of smoke was coming from under the stage.

"Fire! Fire!"

The theater emptied in a few seconds, not without pushing and shoving. However, there was no panic except among the musicians in their balcony. The performers were taken by surprise in their working costumes and scattered squealing out into the street together with the sailors.

It could not have happened at a worse moment: the usual crush of people and cars was increased by the mass exit from the moving-picture houses, and the spectacular arrival of the firemen collected the usual troop of fire enthusiasts.

Anyone who has ever seen the crowds in China knows that between one and five thousand people can appear from nowhere during the first minute and several hundred more at ten-second intervals thereafter. The nude girls did not go unnoticed, and *The South China Telegraph* gleefully reported the proceedings on its front page the next morning.

Propriety, face, the security of the Colony were concerned. On top of it all the parliamentary assistant of the Colonial Secretary was passing through Hong Kong that day.

The Lido closed its doors.

VIII

"Cork your mouth like a bottle; Guard your heart like a rampart."

—CHINESE PROVERB

The affair was disastrous for Mr. Wu and Mr. Lin, the proprietors, for Mr. Pang, the technical director, and for all those who worked in the theater.

Mr. Wu was not worried about the twenty-five thousand dollars he had borrowed from the Sons of Shantung, which had been repaid with interest on the first of September. What distressed him was the loss of the enormous profits just around the corner. Ships of the Seventh Fleet had been coming in with clocklike regularity, much to the credit of their commanders. After the aircraft carriers had come a heavy cruiser, groups of destroyers and transports, and a 45,000-ton battleship that had run out of ammunition along the west coast of Korea.

The fame of the Misses Orchid, Opalescent Moon, Springtime Harmony, Jade Butterfly and Starry Flower had spread from Guam, by way of Okinawa and Sasebo, to Inchon; from the Kuriles, by way of Yokosuka and Keelung, to Subic Bay. The United States Air Force saw no reason for playing second fiddle to the Navy and was said to be planning some recreational visits of its own. On crowded days Mr. Pang had squeezed six shows into the afternoon and four into the evening and had a full house every time. Now, with a trifling fire, all his dreams threatened to go up in smoke.

Mr. Wu was disconsolate, and reproached himself for having failed to take the proper precautions. The theater had been opened in such a hurry that he had neglected to call in Buddhist priests to exorcise the demon and neutralize the evil eye. There was no excuse for such carelessness. One cannot turn a warehouse into a theater without making an effort to appease the evil spirits that are being driven out and the new ones that are waiting to come in. The ceremony would have cost fifty dollars, but what did that matter? What was fifty dollars in comparison to the thousands that were now eluding his grasp?

Four thousand pleasure-bound sailors—how many dollars do they represent, Mr. Lin? If you want a job well done, do it yourself!

Meanwhile Mr. Pang, after several sleepless nights, had thought of a way to retrieve the situation.

IX

"Crows are equally black wherever you find them."

—CHINESE PROVERB

A week after the fire the damage had been repaired and the Lido reopened. Only it was no longer a theater and Lido was not its name. The new sign bore in gold letters on a bright-red background the words "Academy of Far Eastern Art."

The taxi drivers (in return for twenty-five cents for every art lover they brought in) were quick to recommend this new destination. At the door every sailor was given a pencil, often with no lead in it, and a piece of paper. Then he was greeted by Mr. Pang, who had exchanged his tuxedo for a white smock artistically spotted with blobs of ultramarine blue and burnt sienna, a flowing bow tie and a beret. When the room was full, which it usually was within eight minutes after it opened, Miss Orchid and her colleagues posed on the stage, singly and in groups, forming many living pictures in the antique manner, while the art lovers sketched them. Miss Orchid, as intelligent as she was beautiful, had conceived a delightful means of enlivening the lessons and inspiring the students. Between poses the models circulated among them, correcting their crude drawings, with Mr. Pang to interpret their remarks and to add his own:

"Round out that shoulder. Lengthen the right leg. You, sir" (she was addressing Inspector MacIntosh, disguised as a gunner), "your breasts are too high . . . No, now they're too low; take a better look at the model. Broaden the curve of the hip . . ."

As soon as the fame of the Academy of Far Eastern Art reached the headquarters of the United States Air Force in Tokyo, it went ahead with its recreational project, without waiting for authorization from Washington. Had not a 1947 directive from the Pentagon enjoined the overseas commanders to do everything possible to promote culture?

This time Mr. Wu had done things properly. A procession of priests, with gongs, horns, terrifying masks, firecrackers, incense and prayer rolls, came at ten o'clock the first morning to exorcise the evil spirits. They were not satisfied with either the quantity or the quality of the food offered them and demanded nine hundred dollars for their services plus two hundred and seventeen dollars for the incense, firecrackers and other supplementary expenses (for which bills were duly submitted). Fifty dollars, they claimed, was the fee for a struggling new enterprise, but it was obvious that the Academy of Far Eastern Art was in a much higher category and the demons haunting it could not be persuaded to go away for so little. The price asked was actually cut-rate, and there was some danger in shaving it so very close. Mr. Wu was easily persuaded to pay three hundred extra dollars as coverage against every conceivable danger.

"Even if a snake takes refuge in a bamboo tube
His tortuous nature is not altered."

—CHINESE PROVERB

Every conqueror brings in his wake a horde of shopkeepers. The most daring pioneer is bound to be followed by settlers who intend to take over the territory he has thrown open. No inventor is safe from imitators who are always ready to appropriate his ideas.

Mr. Yip, the proprietor of the bar and grill next door to the Academy, could tell a good business deal when he saw one. He was cautious, however, because a grill is one thing and show business is another.

Mr. Lap, whose uncle was the superintendent of the building where the American naval attaché had his office, had fallen madly in love with an actress. She was beautiful enough to raise the poet Su Tung-po from the grave and she could spend her way through the fabulous wealth of the sons of Mr. Ha Ying Tak, the well-known philanthropist who invented Dragon's Balm.

Mr. Yip met Mr. Lap and they clicked. Mr. Lap confided to Mr. Yip his suspicion that Mr. Pang had gone in for selling lemonade, a minor enterprise but one that was sure to be a serious disadvantage to Mr. Yip's business. His southern temperament prompted him to only one conclusion: "This means war. If I could just find a capable partner who really knew show business I'd show Pang what a fight I could give him on his own ground."

"My dear Mr. Yip, look no further, fate has made our paths cross. Come for lunch tomorrow at the studio of the Far Eastern Movie Corporation. I'll introduce you to my friends and in particular to Miss Perfumed Night."

"The great actress? You really mean it?"

"She's my best friend. You'll see, she's not cold at all. She's even more stunning in the flesh than on the screen."

Mr. Yip had some important connections too. Particularly he was on intimate terms with a certain Mr. Kok—their families belonged to different clans but ones that were allied to each other in two neighboring villages in the Pakloh district of Kwangtung. Mr. Kok had come to make his fortune in Hong Kong just after the war and Mr. Yip, who was already well established, had often fed him in times of famine.

Mr. Kok had had the vision to found a small bank in 1948. At the same time, some rich Chinese in Shanghai, Nanking, Tientsin, Hankow, Chungking and other large commercial cities had sniffed the breezes that preceded the winds of revolution. Their instincts came into play and they began to think about investing some of their capital securely but not too far away, and Hong Kong seemed the place. Because this amounted to considerable capital and there were not many banks at the time, the funds of the Kok bank swelled suddenly. The main problem for the bank president became how to make so much money grow.

Mr. Yip had no trouble enlisting the aid of Mr. Kok. And Mr. Lap proceeded to do things in a big way. His first step was to lease the top floor of a brand-new building in the business section and to engage a team of decorators.

"Turn it into a palace," he told them. "Never mind the cost, but remember that I'll go over your bills with a fine-tooth comb."

One room reproduced the throne chamber of the Dragon, another the boudoir of the Phoenix, a third the drawing room of the ladies-in-waiting. A moon-shaped door opened onto a patio filled with rare plants, baroque rock gardens and a fountain whose mosaic basin was filled with exotic fish. The hangings were rainbow-colored and the lights dim.

Many of the rich Chinese who had come to Hong Kong

soon after Mao's takeover had soon decided that it was too near the Marxist paradise to be safe and had moved farther away. But ridiculous passport regulations allowed only their number-one wives to follow. Their concubines were temporarily left behind, lodged in hotel rooms in Kowloon, where they led a tedious existence, with a few trustworthy males to watch over them. It was among these women of the world that Mr. Lap recruited his personnel.

For Mr. Lap and Mr. Yip aspired to reach the officer class. Their studio had the sober name of "Art Pictures, Incorporated," and here officers were taught the art of photographic composition and the latest processes of darkroom development. Any clients who did not own cameras could rent them on the spot. Among the compositions recommended for study were "The Empress readies herself for the game of clouds and rain," "Madame Yang waiting for the Dragons" and "Ducks at the Jade Fountain."

No more than forty-eight hours after the opening, however, the enterprise was broken up by the police and the premises were occupied by a new restaurant. A chartered plane set out from Singapore, stopping at Rangoon, Bangkok, Pnom Penh, Saigon, Manila and Taipei on the way, bearing a committee of husbands empowered to discharge the guards who had been watching over the concubines and to engage new ones. Mr. Kok's bank had to close its doors. Luckily Mr. Kok found a job as a rickshaw driver near the Peninsula. It was not the first time he had experienced such a sudden reversal of fortune.

Meanwhile the Academy of Far Eastern Art, disdainful of rivalry, continued to prosper. Mr. Pang, while remaining the technical director, was deservedly made a full-fledged partner.

XI

"If the roots are pulled up when the grass is cut, there will be no grass the next year."

—CHINESE PROVERB

The Buddhist priests, alas, are not up to date; their lore has not kept pace with modern progress. Newspaper reporters, the demons of today's world, are not listed among the evil spirits dispelled by their exorcism. Toward the end of December 1952 a reporter who had got word of the cultural boom gained admittance to the Academy of Far Eastern Art and wrote it up the next day on the front page of his paper. If the paper had been Chinese no great harm would have been done. Unfortunately the reporter was George Bennett and the paper was the *Hong Kong Chronicle*. And, as luck would have it, a Labour Party leader, Nancy Pierce, M.P., landed that same day at Hong Kong to start an investigation of the functioning of the Crown Colony's legislative council.

A representative of the police informed Messrs. Wu, Lin and Pang, gathered together in the Morris Oxford to receive him, that the Academy of Far Eastern Art must suspend its activities with the least possible delay. For their future guidance he told them, in no uncertain terms, that henceforth naked women could not, under any pretext, be put on display.

XII

"The heart of man is never satisfied. If he obtains the kingdom of Lung, he wants that of Chu also."

—CHINESE PROVERB

Some people grow with defeat. Undaunted amid disaster, armed only with their wits and an iron will, they pluck the banner from the mud, raise it above their heads, and turn a rout into victory. Certain skippers seem almost to desire a storm. Indifferent to complaints from below decks and deaf to pessimistic rumblings from the wardroom, hypnotizing the man at the wheel with their glacial serenity, they bring the ship into port, walk down the gangplank without a word, and go to face their wives with the bad news that they have forgotten to bring back the promised coffee from Maracaibo, where it costs less than chicory.

But Mr. Wu did not belong to this heroic breed. A series of vicissitudes—the warlords (Feng Yu-hsiang, Wu Pei-fu, Chang Tso-lin, to name only the most renowned), the floods of 1925, the southerners, the Japanese occupation, the guerrillas on all sides, the liberation by the Grasshoppers of the Kuomintang, the second liberation by the lovers of the People—all these had served not to strengthen him but to increase his natural anxiety. The loss of the Academy of Far Eastern Art was the last straw. Mr. Lin did his best to comfort him.

"Don't be in such low spirits, Mr. Wu. It's a bitter blow, but you can still trust your friends. We'll come out of it, somehow."

To which Mr. Wu replied:

"The Wise Man has said: 'A rash man goes looking for trouble.' I have saved some money from the catastrophe. And you, my partners, aren't flat broke either. Why should we continue to cudgel our brains?"

Mr. Pang was not steeped in philosophy, but he knew that the best maxims are those inspired by circumstances and, so to speak, made to order.

"But Mr. Wu," he put in, "didn't the Wise Man also say:

'He who stops halfway will never reach Wutaishan?' We can't claim to have reached the sacred mountain when we still have a fortune to make."

"Mr. Pang, and you too, Mr. Lin, I know some things that you don't know. My friend the banker, Mr. Han, president of the Sons of Shantung, told me last month that there is danger of a declaration of peace in Korea. And it's his job to be well informed. He told me that if the American general, Eisenhower, were to become president of the United States the war would soon be over. And Eisenhower has been elected. A man must be alert to the signs of the times. There's not much time left for profit-taking, perhaps no more than a month or two. Then the American sailors will go home. It's no use fighting fate."

Over the objections of the younger members of its board of directors the company was dissolved. Performers and technicians were summoned to a banquet at the Seaview Hotel, where generous drinks and an offer of severance pay softened the impact of the loss of their jobs. Mr. Wu left the management of the restaurant to Mr. Kao and retired to his new country house by the sea, near Saikung, in the New Territories. On the advice of Mr. Han he put his remaining capital into a corset factory, whose products were made not for the benefit of Chinese women, who do not need them, but for a promising export trade. Mr. Lin bought a 25 per cent interest in a new moving-picture house at Kowloon. As for Mr. Pang, he went to take a rest at Lantao.

XIII

"A word whispered among men
Echoes in the sky like thunder."

—CHINESE PROVERB

On a large-scale map the island of Lantao is seen to be some miles west of Hong Kong but still in British territorial waters. A ferry makes the trip in an hour and a half, once a day. The passenger disembarks on a rickety pier thrown up on the muddy beach and finds himself a hundred years removed from the noise of the city, from the clang-clang of the trolleys, the zing-zing of the telephones, and the tap-tap of the mahjong parties. Lantao has remained just as it was in the last century when the British planted their flag there in order to cover the western approaches to the Hong Kong harbor. It is a rustic, green haven, made up of a few scattered groups of fishermen, who spend their lives between their junks and their pile-supported shacks, and a few farming villages in the valleys of the interior. There is no road and no electricity.

A Buddhist monastery, as remote as if it were in Tibet, is tucked away in a hollow on the side of the mountain that is the island's highest point. It was there that Mr. Pang took up lodgings. Awakened at the break of day by the gong calling the monks to prayer, he went to wash in the well in the courtyard. Then he sat down at a granite table under a spreading umbrella pine and ate a breakfast of soya biscuits and tea, served by a young novice. He went through a ritual of Chinese gymnastics, listening all the while to the hum of prayers from the temple and the musical clinking of the bells on the rooftops. A long walk on the mountain paths gave him an appetite for dinner, a strictly vegetarian but delicious repast. As soon as it was dark he went to bed. Above all, he meditated.

At the end of a week, physically and spiritually cleansed, he took ceremonious leave of the abbot, left an offering of a hundred dollars for the support of the monastery and its holy men, and took the ferry back to Hong Kong.

REPORT

by Inspector Ian MacIntosh, first flying squad of the Royal Hong Kong Police Force

Re: The Orient Shoeshine Parlor.

Follow-up of verbal instructions from Chief-inspector Graham of the R.H.K.P.F., supplemented by Deputy Commissioner Sullivan, chief of police of the Second District (Hong Kong, northwest).

1. Today, 17 January 1953, according to the instructions specified above, I put on the uniform of a petty officer, U. S. Navy, procured by the Special Branch. A taxi driven by Detective Li, playing the part of driver, took me to 72 Nanking Road, where the doorman gave Detective Li twenty-five cents.

2. The "Orient Shoeshine Parlor" occupies the ground floor of a five-story apartment house. The panes of the three windows have been covered with red paint so that it is impossible to see from the street what is going on inside.

3. About fifty U. S. sailors were standing in line in the entrance hall. My arrival was greeted with whistles, probably because I was the only petty officer present. A European, in civilian dress, was a few places ahead of me in the line. He was turned back at the far end of the hall by a Chinese at a swinging gate, who seemed to be scrutinizing the customers. I heard him say in English to the European: "Sorry, for Navy only."

4. I went through the gate without any trouble. After that I had to go to a ticket window, where I was asked for six Hong Kong dollars. I paid with one U. S. dollar and one Hong Kong dollar, which added up to six dollars and eighty cents according to the current rate of exchange. The cashier gave me back no change.

5. I entered the establishment. It consists of a large room, about thirty by twenty feet. Running along the walls there is a platform about a foot high and two feet wide on which, at three-inch intervals, there are forty-six wooden chairs.

6. I waited until a chair was empty and then sat down. Fourteen young Chinese girls, each one with a small wooden stool and a box of brushes, made the rounds of the room, from chair to chair, shining the customers' shoes.

7. They were clothed from head to foot in transparent nylon raincoats. They wore absolutely no other article of dress. All of them are very pretty. The youngest seemed to be about eighteen years old, the oldest twenty-five. Among them I identified several performers from the Lido—including Miss Orchid, Miss Springtime Harmony, Miss Pine Balm and Miss Opalescent Moon. I also recognized two of the models who used to work at Art Pictures, Incorporated (cf. Inspector Yen's report of Nov. 12, 1952, regarding certain concubines repudiated by their husbands).

8. A sign at the far end of the room reads: "For your enjoyment and for the sake of your friends after you, please be quiet and well behaved. Thank you. The Management." The customers, for

the most part, heeded this warning, contenting themselves with looking at the employees, exchanging whispered comments on their figures, and changing places in order to obtain the services of the girl they liked best. A loudspeaker emits a steady stream of dance music.

9. Two incidents took place during my visit. When it was the turn of a sailor sitting next to me he pulled his trousers up to his knees, disclosing a pair of high-laced boots, which aroused laughter among his companions and protests from the girls. The sailor insisted on having his boots shined. "I brought them all the way from Japan on purpose, so don't make a fuss," he said. A Chinaman, attracted by the noise, came in through a door at the far end of the room, and I identified him as Pang Fen-tien, formerly technical director of the Lido and a partner in the Academy of Far Eastern Art (cf. my reports of June 2 and October 22, 1952, on these two establishments). He asked for silence, and the matter was settled by the payment of an extra six Hong Kong dollars.

10. The second incident occurred when the employee at the gate burst into the room, shouting: "*Ching Cha Lai, Ching Cha Lai!* (Cheese it, the cops!). The girls disappeared in the twinkle of an eye and were replaced by young boys, who came in through the same doors as they had gone out. A few minutes later, when it all turned out to be a false alarm, the girls returned to their stations.

11. After my shoes had been quite competently shined I left the parlor. During the nineteen min-

utes of my visit I saw nothing improper except the girls' dress. None of the sailors went through the three doors at the far end of the room, which must lead to offices and private living quarters.

Signed: I. MacIntosh.

XIV

"A rat's teeth don't produce ivory."

—CHINESE PROVERB

The morning of February 6, 1953, marked the beginning of one of those superb Hong Kong winter days that precede the drizzles and downpours of spring. The sky was blue, the air brisk and the sun delightfully warm. Leslie Barrington-Jones was eating breakfast (papaya juice, porridge, kippers, toast, marmalade and tea) on the balcony of his apartment, halfway up the Peak, with a view of the harbor.

He cast a speculative look at the dark-gray silhouette of the American aircraft carrier anchored in front of the Royal Hong Kong Yacht Club, but the main focus of his attention was the *Hong Kong Chronicle* and, more particularly, the column entitled "Hong Kong, Day by Day," which began:

Curious spirits, and there are many of them, are wondering how our friendly visitors, who are and always will be welcome among us ["The filthy hypocrite!" Leslie muttered to himself] *are managing to amuse themselves since the closing of the Lido and the Academy of Far Eastern Art. But they need not worry. Our reporter, George Bennett* ["The Bastard!"] *contrived to enter a most unusual shoeshine parlor on Nanking Road. This was his third attempt to visit the new establishment, which seems to be inaccessible to civilians and open only to those wearing the uniform of Uncle Sam. Yesterday George Bennett got hold of this indispensable outfit* ["Illegal impersonation of a member of the armed forces of an ally; I'll have to ask our legal adviser how *that* will stand up in court!"]. *As a result he was able to get his shoes shined by a bevy of beautiful girls, with or without bathing suits, every one of them a potential candidate for the title of Miss Hong Kong. Technically, the girls are dressed. But although George Bennett does not—alas!—have X-ray eyes* ["the idiot!"] *he had a full view of their charms from every possible angle.*

'Which one would win your vote?' we asked him.

'Impossible to decide in five minutes. But I'm going back this evening.'

Then George told us how he had learned about the place. The other day, on the Star Ferry, he had heard two British sailors complain of the unaccustomed luster of their Yankee comrades' shoes. 'Already they've taken up bagpipe playing,' one of them remarked. 'But when they go in for a high polish of their shoes, like ours, that's the end!'

Leslie sighed, folded the paper, tucked it into his brief-case, put out his cigarette, cast a parting look at the air-craft carrier, and went off to his office.

The next day Inspector Chao, a native of Weihaiwei, a former British base in Shantung, presented a calling card to Mr. Pang. He had come, he said, on a purely friendly visit, inspired by the fact that they both came from the same province. How was Mrs. Pang, he inquired. Oh, she had gone to join her ancestors. And Mrs. Chao? Very well, in spite of the fact that she complained about the Hong Kong climate and continued to hanker after her native Shantung, which she had left sixteen years before.

Ah, Shantung!

And what about Mr. Pang's children? Well, there was no news of them. They had stayed behind, and Inspector Chao would be the first to understand that writing to them could serve only to get them in trouble.

Mr. Chao understood very well. And how about business?

It was hard sledding, incredibly hard to earn one's daily bowl of rice. If a man didn't feel a moral obligation to stand by his employees—all of them refugees—instead of driving them to beg in the streets he'd be much happier to let everything go . . . There are so many sharks in the business world and so little protection against them. They're always after something or other, and what do they give in return? Only worthless promises. And protection was what a business like Mr. Pang's needed. Of course, he was ready to make any sacrifice to obtain it, that is, if the protection was really efficacious and the sacrifices were within the realm of the possible. But to what did Mr. Pang owe the honor of Mr. Chao's visit?

Mr. Chao took a sip of tea.

"I'm sorry to tell you, Mr. Pang, that the authorities would like to see you close down your shoeshine parlor. It's not that your enterprising spirit isn't appreciated. It's worthy of the great strategist, Chu Ko-liang. And your disinterested efforts to please our American friends deserve nothing but praise. But the fact is that there are some very unpleasant people who wield considerable influence among us. And the authorities can't afford to rub them the wrong way."

The inspector took a second sip of tea. In spite of belonging to the vice squad he was not lacking in social graces. Resolutely refusing the hundred-dollar bill that Mr. Pang offered him for his favorite charity, he assured him once more of his esteem. Then, making a series of ceremonial bows and protesting, as convention demanded, that his host should not pay him the excessive honor of accompanying him to the door, he went away.

Mr. Pang sold the furnishings and equipment of the shoeshine parlor, at a good price, to a business group from Szechwan. He gave his employees two weeks of severance pay and took the ferry to Lantao.

XV

"Woman's virtue knows no limits;
Likewise woman's anger."

—CHINESE PROVERB

Chief-Inspector Graham burst into laughter when MacIntosh entered his office.

"What in the world has happened to you, old man? You look like a spotted horse."

"It's this wretched hair dye, sir. Guaranteed to wash out, but after two hours of soaping my head, this is the result. You won't laugh when I tell you that I had to order this sombrero from Lane, Crawford and chalk up thirty-five dollars on my expense account. Here's the bill; I leave it you to explain to Her Majesty's accounting office. Meanwhile, I'm submitting my report."

"Thanks. Sit down while I look it over. But first let's do something about your hair. Are you busy this evening. No? Good enough."

Graham dialed a telephone number.

"Hello, is that you, Maggie? I have a problem. Do you know how to get dye out of hair? With just a regular shampoo? But what if it doesn't work? Vinegar, you say? Get some vinegar, then. I'm bringing MacIntosh home to dinner, and he'll need your help."

REPORT

by Inspector Ian MacIntosh, first flying squad of the Royal Hong Kong Police Force

Re: Chinese Rapid Laundry, Ltd.

Follow-up of verbal instructions from Chief-inspector Graham of the R.H.K.P.F., supplemented by Deputy Commissioner Lowell, chief of police of the Second District (Kowloon, southeast).

1. Today, 27 February, 1953, according to the instructions specified above, I put on the uniform of a supply clerk, U. S. Navy, procured by the

Special Branch. I had previously dyed my hair black (it is naturally red) and completed my disguise with a false moustache.

2. After disembarking from the Star Ferry at Kowloon I hailed a taxi from the stand in front of the Peninsula Hotel and, assuming an American accent, asked the driver to take me to the laundry. "What laundry, sir?" "The thing-um-a-bob laundry, you know the one I mean." "There are over a hundred laundries in Kowloon, sir." "I know of only one." "But which one?" "I don't know the name." The driver consulted the other drivers, who had gathered around us. They, too, didn't seem to know what laundry I meant. "O.K.," I replied; "I'll find it myself," and I walked away.

3. As no Chinese taxi driver has ever been known to refuse a passenger because of not knowing where he wanted to go, it must be concluded that there is some sort of understanding between the Chinese Rapid Laundry, Ltd. and the association of taxi drivers.

4. I proceeded to the corner of Nathan Road and Lancaster Street, where I found the taxi driven by Detective Li, suitably disguised, waiting for me. Detective Li put me down on a street parallel to Canton Road, some hundred yards from the Chinese Rapid Laundry.

5. This laundry is at the far end of a courtyard behind No. 198 Canton Road. There are no windows in front, and at one side of the door there is a sign with the name and the words: "Rapid Laundry. Clothes pressed while you wait. Especially recommended for the U. S. Navy."

6. A Chinese employee was sitting on a chair and asked me, in English: "What do you want?" I answered with the password indicated by Deputy Commissioner Lowell: "I want good service." He took a key out of his pocket and opened a gate, five or six feet high, about a yard distant from the front of the laundry.

7. The gate opened onto a winding hall about thirty feet long, where a dozen or so American sailors and petty officers were standing in line. I waited for a quarter of an hour, during which time some of the sailors made rude remarks: "Dig the moustache on this guy! Our old man would rub it off if he ever got duty on the *Cedar Rapids!*" "Hell! Those kind never go to sea; they'd rather warm a chair all day and goose Waves." "Hey, Mac; ain't those Waves enough for you? You want to tickle some Chinks with your moustache?" I kept quiet so that my accent would not give me away, and went on chewing my gum and staring at the laundry door.

8. Beyond the door I gave eight dollars to a cashier. An employee came up and asked what he could do for me. "I want to get a handkerchief ironed," I told him. "Certainly, sir, right away. Just wait over here." He led me into one of the twelve compartments off the waiting-room. Each one of them was closed off by a burlap curtain, whose dimensions are such as to leave the customer's head and feet visible from the outside.

9. A few seconds later the same employee came back with an attractive young Chinese girl whom I could not immediately identify. "This young

woman has brought in some laundry," he told me. "Do you mind if she waits with you?" "Not a bit. Delighted!" He drew the curtain behind us.

10. The girl smiled at me and started to disrobe. She took off her dress, slip, panties and brassière in quick succession and handed them over the curtain to the employee.

11. The girl was standing in front of me, and finally I pushed forward a chair, the only one in the compartment. She smiled again and said in Chinese (Mandarin): "*Leng, leng,*" which means "cold." I pretended not to understand. Then she went into an act, shivering and making a sound of *brrr*. I asked her, in English, whether she wanted me to warm her up. To which she replied "*Pu tung*" ("I don't understand"). I went closer and put my arms around her. She struggled to free herself and cried: "No, no!" The employee, followed by a man whom I identified as Pang Fen-tien (see my reports of June 2 and October 22, 1952, and January 17, 1953, on the Lido, the Academy of Far Eastern Art, and the Orient Shoeshine Parlor), burst in on us. The employee said, in English: "Look, O.K.; no touch, O.K.?" I couldn't talk, because my false moustache had fallen down over my mouth while the girl was resisting me and I had to cover it with my hand. But I nodded to show that I had understood, and Pang Fen-tien and his employee went away.

12. It really was cold, and the girl was trembling. I motioned to her to get back into her dress (which the employee had returned to her), and she did so, saying, in English: "You good boy."

With my hand over my mouth I blew up my cheeks and tried to put across the idea that I had a toothache. We were having a spirited conversation, by means of deaf-and-dumb signs, when the employee returned. He gave the girl her underwear and me my handkerchief. I waited for her to get dressed, then gave her a two-dollar tip and went away. She slipped out through a door in the room outside.

13. I went, on foot, to the Hangchow Restaurant on Nathan Road, where I shut myself up in the washroom and refastened my moustache. I then returned to the Chinese Rapid Laundry and said I wanted my socks washed. The Chinese girl who wanted her clothes washed at the same time turned out to be Miss Orchid (see the reports mentioned just above). I tried to embrace her, but she struck me across the face and my moustache again became unstuck, so that I was obliged to repeat the pretense of having a toothache to prevent my disguise from falling off completely. Pang Fen-tien arrived once more upon the scene, apologizing for not having washed my socks because the machine was out of order. Then he asked me to go away. I indicated that I wanted a refund of my money, which he duly returned before escorting me to the door.

Signed: I. MacIntosh.

"Quite a report!" said Graham approvingly when he had finished reading. "This Miss Orchid is a regular wildcat, isn't she? I hope she didn't hit you too hard."

MacIntosh blushed, but his already ruddy complexion did not betray him. He forced a smile.

"No, Chief-Inspector," he said. "Her slap in the face wasn't so bad. The fact is . . ."

"Well, what?"

"Look here, sir, there are some risks that a fellow is ready to take. But there are others we were never told about at the Police Academy. Just put yourself in my shoes. I mean, she's a damned pretty girl."

"I see . . . If my wife succeeds in fixing your hair I'll send you to spend the weekend in Macao. You need some relaxation."

"Thank you, sir. What I really need is another case."

"What do you mean? Look here, Ian, you're doing a first-rate job, and your reports are being read and appreciated in high places. You're twenty-seven years old, and Chief-Inspector Barnes is about to be shifted to Kenya. I've already spoken to the deputy superintendent about the possibility of your taking his place, and he reacted favorably. Surely you're not losing your nerve just because some Chinese girls have shed their clothes in front of you!"

"Thank you, sir. I really appreciate your goodwill."

"Think nothing of it. I'm acting for the good of the service. But I don't want you in Hong Kong this weekend, is that clear? On Monday you can tell me all about Macao."

Graham pushed a button and a uniformed police officer came into the room.

"Yen, two photostats of this report right away. One, by scooter, to Government House, the other to the Commissioner."

Then, turning again to MacIntosh:

"By the way, you'd better grow a real moustache. It looks as if you may need it with all these bloody reporters around."

No official report contains a complete story. What MacIntosh had left out was the fact that when Miss Orchid struck him he very nearly lost his self-control. This was quite out of the ordinary, because he'd suffered much harder blows on the football field, without the same consequences. He'd actually wanted to kiss the girl, unofficially. If Pang Fen-tien hadn't arrived on the scene he would have done it. What a pretty little piece she was, delicate and aristocratic and passionate all at once. Her eyes and nose, and those transparent ears that he had suddenly wanted so much to kiss . . .

In the hall MacIntosh ran into Detective Li and beckoned to him to come to his office.

"Li . . ."

"Yes, sir."

"Do you know the girl who works for Pang Fen-tien, the one called 'Miss Orchid'?"

Li reflected, then his face lit up, and his hands traced a broad curve at the height of his chest.

"Is that the one you mean, sir?"

"No, I mean the one like this," and MacIntosh brought his hand down almost vertically.

"Yes, sir; I see, sir."

"I want to know all about her."

"Yes, sir. She lives with other refugees from Szechwan, on Diamond Hill, and . . ."

"Bring me in a full report on Monday, will you?"

"Yes, sir; understood, sir."

XVI

"If observance of the law is your only policy in making a living, even gold won't find you a partner."

—CHINESE PROVERB

Mr. Ku had been on the board commissioned by the husbands in exile to take stock of the deportment of the concubines provisionally left behind in Hong Kong, and to make all necessary decisions on the absentees' behalf.

Mr. Ku had been an important businessman in Chungking before he made a second success at Singapore. His native city of Chungking was in Szechwan and, as everybody knows, that province is a land of rats and people so shrewd that, collectively, they are nicknamed all over China "the rats of Szechwan."

The inquiry into the unfaithfulness of some of the concubines was conducted briskly, but as a by-product Mr. Ku acquired the information that Art Pictures, Inc. was set up on a fundamentally sound economic basis. Its failure was undoubtedly attributable to the promoters' ineptness.

Mr. Ku was a busy man. A deal involving a hundred thousand tons of contraband rubber to be brought out of Surabaya was urgently waiting at Singapore. Thus he went to find Mr. Kang, the Secretary of the Sons of Szechwan at Hong Kong. He handed him seventy-two thousand dollars withdrawn the day before from Kok's bank, gave him some brief instructions and took the plane back.

Thereupon Mr. Kang assembled a group of his business friends. They gave the matter some thought and soon put their finger on what they thought had gone wrong with the romantic schemes of Mr. Pang (who, after all, was a dense brute from Shantung) and likewise with the affairs of those vulgar Cantonese, Mr. Yip and Mr. Lap. Playing with the law, especially as administered by the "Big Noses," is as crazy as pulling the whiskers of a tiger. That is as obvious as a louse on the head of a newborn infant. Hong Kong is not China!

They, on the contrary, took care to obtain an authoritative interpretation of the law. For this purpose they engaged the services of Mr. Frederick Fak, one of Hong Kong's leading lawyers, who confirmed what they had suspected all along, namely that females must be decently dressed. Like Chinese ladies? Exactly. Or like European ladies, attending a ball at the Hong Kong Club? Even better!

Here, then, is the formula they contrived. Place the following advertisement in the Hong Kong Chinese papers:

> Important Southeast Asian airline seeks hostesses, attractive, educated, with high moral standards. English language essential. Send applications and photographs to Box No. . . .

Hire two secretaries to sort out the avalanche of replies. Then engage the best refugee dressmaker.

Have her cut to measure, for each successful candidate, a silk dress. The lower half tightly fitted, Chinese style, with openings on either side to above the knees; the upper half modeled on a European ball gown, completely off the shoulders and with a plunging neckline. Seat the hostesses, in these dresses, on low stools, and place the chairs of the gentlemen customers on a 12-inch-high platform, from which they will enjoy a view hardly less seductive than the one banned by the law.

As if by magic you have the Asiatic Shoeshine House, at 26 Prince Alexander Street. It takes capital to set up an establishment of this kind, you will say. Of course it does. But you have to do things in a big way if you want to make money.

What if peace breaks out in Korea? Ridiculous! Only the Americans are ingenuous enough to imagine that the

Communists seriously want to negotiate. And the reporters! Invite them to come see. Publicity won't hurt, because everything is perfectly legal. And the British are sticklers for legality.

And that was just how it went, especially the publicity. This time George Bennett of the *Hong Kong Chronicle* was not alone. After the authorities had read the despatches from Reuters, Havas, the Associated Press, DNB, Michi Machi and the rest, a conference was called at Government House, which, according to all accounts, was long and stormy.

The sequel was a police raid at 26 Prince Alexander Street. But it was discovered that the Asiatic Shoeshine House had fully complied with the letter of the law. What was to be done? If the Governor were to evoke his emergency powers and close the place down, Mr. Frederick Fak would alert his Labour Party friends in the House of Commons. And, on second thought, closing the Asiatic Shoeshine House would reopen the case of Mr. Pang Fentien. It would endanger the continuation of the visits from the Seventh Fleet, which had so contributed to the prosperity and hence to the political stability of the Crown Colony. And yet this kind of thing could not be allowed to go on. If the Asiatic Shoeshine House were successful a dozen other places like it would spring into being, and Hong Kong would become as notorious as Macao. H. E. simply nodded reflectively, and kept on nodding.

Bobo finally saved the situation. At a party given for the officers of a South Korean frigate (no boost to the economy there!) Leslie informed him, between two gimlets, of the impasse of the Government House consultations.

"Is that what's got you down? I can take care of it right away."

And Commodore Sir Bernard Leighton-Parker led the diplomatic adviser to the United States naval attaché to the other end of the room.

"Dickie, old boy, I must ask you a favor."

"Anything you want, Bobo."

"Do you suppose you could declare a place called the Asiatic Shoeshine House off-limits to your Navy personnel?" And, lowering his voice, he added: "A shady dive, really—probably financed by the Communists, you know, listening post and all that sort of thing."

"No problem, Bobo. First thing in the morning. Thanks for the tip. Our people have such big mouths . . ."

"Ours too. That's why I wanted to give you the gen."

The Asiatic Shoeshine House had just succumbed to a fatal attack of "old boy-ism."

Curiously enough, Mr. Kang disappeared completely. The Society of the Sons of Sqechuan made cautious but complete enquiries about their missing secretary. Mr. Kang was revealed to have been a communist agent, in fact head of a whole Intelligence branch; he was discovered to be presently assisting the construction of the new Lanchow-Urunchi railway, following the sabotage of an important mission in Hong Kong.

XVII

"Pleasure is skin-deep;
Sorrow is embedded in the heart."

—CHINESE PROVERB

The crossing from Hong Kong to Macao lasts only three hours, but its beauty is unforgettable. The ferry winds its way through a maze of fantastically shaped islands, a sort of Bay of Along, where the myriad cargo junks and fishing craft, with their patched dirty-yellow and blue sails seem to belong to another planet.

MacIntosh had often made this voyage, and always with pleasure, although he could not but regret the time, not so long past, when these waters were infested with Chinese pirates and the Royal Navy had the time of its life chasing them. Now he remained, indifferently, in the bar. Not even a glance at the young English couple tenderly embracing on the deck, newlyweds going to spend their honeymoon at Macao.

Once ashore he went to the Hotel Praya. No sooner was he installed in his room than there was a knock at the door and the bellboy proposed a "nice girl." Once upon a time his response would have been automatic. It was to the use of these bedmate dictionaries that he owed his mastery of the Chinese tongue. The only trouble was that one invariably fell asleep on the same page. But today he showed no interest. He took a Chinese book out of his bag and tried to decipher it, but the meaning escaped him. Then he stretched out on the bed with an Agatha Christie novel, but after a few pages he laid it down and attempted in vain to take a nap. A hot shower was equally ineffectual. Finally he put on his clothes and went out.

The animation of the streets, the mixture of Latin and Chinese elements, the Portuguese signs, the soldiers from Angola, the fireworks and match factories, the fish market, the traffic of junks along the canals, the vicinity of Communist China, none of these had the power to distract him. Finding himself in front of the post office, he went in and bought a set of the latest local stamps, which were sure to give pleasure to his friends back in Dundee. Ten minutes well spent. For a moment he thought of dropping in on his friend the chief of police, Pereira de Souza. But halfway to this goal he changed his mind and decided that he would rather be alone. He went into a tavern and drank a bottle of the sharp-tasting Portuguese wine, known as "Blood of the Virgin." Back at the hotel he took another shower and thought of dining at a Chinese restaurant. Rejecting this idea, he lingered in the melancholy game rooms, where a dozen coolies were gambling a few pennies, lowering them in baskets to the croupiers on the floor below. An open drug store provided him with some sleeping pills, and he took two of them before trying, once more unsuccessfully, to go to sleep. He rang for the bellboy and told him "I want a nice girl," but when the boy brought her to him he gave her a generous tip and sent her away.

He was just dozing off when there were repeated knocks at the door. Cursing to himself, he got up and opened it. With all the impetus of the front line of the New Zealand rugby team, a dozen girls pushed their way into the room.

"Choose, Mister," said the bellboy. "Mister turn down nice girl half an hour ago. I lose face."

The image of Miss Orchid peopled MacIntosh's dreams all night long. He took the early morning ferry back to Hong Kong, remaining once more, for the full length of the crossing, in the bar. He made it a point not even to glance at the young Portuguese couple tenderly embracing on the deck, newlyweds going to spend their honeymoon at Hong Kong.

XVIII

"The man who doesn't look ahead is sure to find trouble around the corner."

—CHINESE PROVERB

The Hong Kong Club, a gray cathedral in the Edwardian colonial style, occupies a huge quadrangle at the eastern end of the business section between the cricket field, the harbor, a parking lot and the naval base. It is a strategic spot on the path taken by people leaving their offices to go back up to their villas on the Peak. Thus everyone in Hong Kong connected with finance, business, government, the armed services, industry and the bar (this is the pecking order) can be found there after five o'clock every day.

For the most part, the club is strictly British. Foreigners, unable to assimilate the traditions that seem to drip from the walls, do not feel at ease. As for the Chinese, they are not admitted. This is not entirely because the board clings to outdated taboos, but because it is still essential for the white man to have a refuge in this faraway land. The "Chinese friends" are free to have their own clubs closed to whites, and indeed they have them.

The club has two main doors that women may not enter save once a year, on the occasion of the grand ball. Usually they have to come in by another door that admits them, through a labyrinth of long corridors, into the two rooms where they are amiably tolerated. These rooms are of course as far away as possible from the two holy of holies: the noisy and lively bar and the cavernous and silent reading room. It is unthinkable that males should be disturbed if they want to relax for two or three hours in the solitude of the library or that they should feel a disapproving eye fixed on them if thirst drives them to order an eighth gimlet. Mr. Chase, the attorney for China Motors, was usually the first to arrive at the club; he had only to cross the street. He had a ritual: in the reading room a comfortable leather chair near the fireplace where in winter there was an artificial electric coal fire, a Pimms

Number One, his favorite drink, which the boy served him automatically, and the latest issue of *Punch.* Between cartoons he glanced at the hall, watching for his habitual partners. Only when all three had come into the bar did he join them for a long game of liar's dice: each player hides his dice under the shaker and calls out something higher than the preceding player until someone decides to challenge.

That evening Bill Crabb, the accountant, and Colonel Wynn (retired), a collector of tropical butterflies, came to fetch him instead of waiting at the bar.

"What's up?" asked Hutch Chase after they had left the library. Colonel Wynn put out his hand: "Twenty dollars."

"I've lost?"

"Yes, sir."

"Is it official?"

"Not yet, but the same as. Baron has already paid up."

"What did they dream up this time?"

"A laundry where the Chinese clients undress in front of the sailors."

"I'll be hanged! And the police broke it up?"

Fred Baron, the stockbroker, was getting impatient holding his shaker.

"Are you coming or not?" he asked.

They took their usual table and the dice were thrown.

"I begin," said Fred. "Two pair, with kings."

"With aces," said Hutch. "The police broke it up?"

"That's another story," the colonel answered. "Three nines. The police are always the last to know."

"Three little tens," Bill Crabb announced. "We've got our own informants, though."

Fred Baron bounced in his chair, crying: "Full house of jacks with queens."

Hutch cautiously put two dice under his shaker and rolled; an ace and a ten came up. He called out something higher. "Full house of jacks with kings. Was it the reporters who told you about it?"

The colonel sneered: "Reporters! There they are, poking their noses in everything, buying drinks for sailors, bribing taxi drivers, promising pay for whoever gives them a lead. A bunch of nitwits!"

"What's your shot?" Baron interrupted.

"It's my turn? All right then, I'll see you," said the colonel. Hutch raised his shaker. He had four aces. Crestfallen, the colonel took a chip.

All the players shook their shakers and slammed them noisily down on the table. The colonel said without looking, "Three tens. Mind you, they'll end up by getting a clue. The Chinese will keep quiet, but some sailor will start blabbing."

"Three jacks," said Bill Crabb.

"It's scandalous," said Hutch.

"What is?"

"The police—look at them! It's shocking that they can't manage to make themselves respected by the Chinese. Oh, I know! You liberal people find the story amusing. I know the Chinese and I'm telling you this: let them find a crack to crawl through, they'll widen it, and tomorrow when there are no more law and order in the Colony you'll come crying. If I were governor, I'd long ago . . ."

"Listen to the reactionary on his soap box! And what shot does the reactionary call? We're playing liar's dice, gentlemen, don't forget."

"The reactionary says three kings."

"I'll see it," said Bill Crabb.

Mr. Chase had only a pair of jacks. He took a chip.

"If you play like that, it's not surprising that you lose all your bets," the colonel said to tease him.

"I've lost twenty dollars, but I'll gladly bet a hundred that when they finally arrest those Chinese of yours again, they'll be through. Come on, now, they're not all that clever."

"I'll take that bet," said the colonel.

"Me too," said Bill Crabb.

"Me too, but on Hutch's side," said Fred Baron. "Boy, a G.T."

"What are you betting on over there?" asked Mr. Shelton from the next table.

Bill Crabb explained: "Hutch and Fred bet a hundred dollars that the Chinese won't find another gimmick."

"Two hundred dollars with them," Mr. Shelton offered.

"I put a hundred on the Chinese," said Mr. Lewys from the same table.

"Just a sec," said Bill Crabb, taking a notebook out of his pocket.

When he had finished marking it, three thousand four hundred and fifty dollars had been bet on the police and two thousand seven hundred on the Chinese.

Mr. Pang was not one of those unfortunates who, born with silver spoons in their mouths, begin their careers as vice-presidents and end it as clerks. Even without the benefit of business-school training he knew—and experience had borne him out—that no enterprise can develop, or merely survive, unless provision has been made for an emergency, and a plan, better still two plans, have been laid to circumvent it.

While searching for an idea he needed to be easy in his mind, to find someone with whom to share his problems. None of his employees was qualified to play such a role, except perhaps Miss Orchid. One evening, as he was taking her back to Diamond Hill, he had a sudden inspiration. Why could she not take on some of the responsibilities of the laundry? Point-blank he asked her.

"Of course," was her reply.

The only question was whether she could keep the turbulent sailors as well as the employees under control.

"Of course," she said again.

After a short trial had confirmed Miss Orchid's executive ability, Mr. Pang left the laundry completely in her hands and took the bus to Saikung.

The Saikung road, built before the war for military reasons, is so narrow that it is open to traffic one way, in alternating directions during the odd and even hours. While the bus moved along Mr. Pang understood more clearly why Mr. Wu had chosen to end his days at the end of the line: it was Shantung, even down to the temperature. A broken coastline with coves and creeks, little islands, lagoons, golden sand and a green mountain in the background.

Mr. Pang made a note in passing of the Hakka peasant women's costumes: a hat made of a narrow circular band of woven bamboo with a fringe of black tissue coming down all around it, and a hole in the center out of which came the hair; a black blouse of light material and trousers the same. Miss Precious Treasure would do very well in such an outfit the day when a strip-tease show could be opened legally.

The village did not spread very far. There were a hundred or so fishermen's cottages and a few sparsely patronized stores. The passer-by whom Mr. Pang asked about Mr. Wu's house spoke with a strong Shantung accent.

"Aren't we compatriots?" asked Mr. Pang. "My miserable home town is Tsingtas. What is your glorious home town?"

"I came here from Weihaiwei with my family when I was very little," replied second-class secret serviceman Ch'eng.

"And what is your honorable profession?"

"I gather wood from the mountain. I'm going just now in the direction of the Wu house."

Mr. Wu's house of solid gray brick, with a roof whose tiles were upcurved in order to catch evil spirits by hooking their pant-seats, was hidden in a little valley in the midst of bamboos and pines.

"Mr. Wu is at the beach," said the gardener.

"It's this way," said second-class secret serviceman Ch'eng. "I was just on my way there."

They found Mr. Wu on the beach, sitting at a folding table under a bamboo parasol. With his glasses on his nose he was staring out at the sea. From time to time he daubed a piece of rice paper with his paintbrush.

Mr. Pang saw that he was painting geese.

"I'm not like modern painters," said Mr. Wu once the greetings were over. "I don't need to look at nature to copy it. I have my inspiration here." He thumped energetically on his stomach, the seat of his artistic inspiration. "Tomorrow I'll take you to the little island across there where there is a beautiful beach with all sorts of shells. I'll teach you to paint parrots, it's very easy."

Second-class secret serviceman Ch'eng was not only a

woodman but also a shellfisherman. He was already at work on the island the next day when Mr. Pang and Mr. Wu got off the sampan. Mr. Pang bought from him a bucket of clams, and then they got down to talking seriously, about Mr. Pang's business worries, about the endless Panmunjom negotiations, about the rental of a five-room apartment at Kowloon, about whether there was a real estate agent who came from Tsingtas, and what Mr. Wu thought of the president of the association of tailors accredited to the United States Navy.

When Mr. Pang thanked Mr. Wu for his hospitality and, on the sixth evening, took the bus from Kowloon, he had learned to paint parrots, geese, cabbages and bamboo shoots.

Ever since the abrupt closing of the Academy of Far Eastern Art Mr. Pang had subscribed to all the English-language newspapers of the Crown Colony. He scanned them every morning at breakfast, from the local news to the despatches at Panmunjom. When he read one day in the *Hong Kong Chronicle* an interview with an American sailor, describing in detail the Chinese Rapid Laundry, he calmly seasoned his noodles with red-pepper sauce and warned Miss Orchid of the probability of a visit—of a purely private nature—from a certain Inspector Chao. She was to bring the inspector directly to his office and serve tea.

XIX

"When you catch a thief, seize
the booty;
When you catch an adulterer,
be sure you get his partner as
well."

—CHINESE PROVERB

Three blasts of the horn, two short and one long, told MacIntosh that Detective Li was waiting below with his fake taxi. He paused only long enough to check the details of his disguise. Dark, crew-cut hair, shaved up the back of his head, steel-rimmed glasses, an open package of Pall Malls and a Zippo lighter in his blouse pocket, a gold ring with the black enamel seal of Lincoln College on the fourth finger of his right hand. In front of the mirror over the fireplace he practiced the Cary Grant salute, which a recent film had popularized as the latest fashion: the hand with the palm turned outward straight in front of the face, then a semi-circular movement of the forearm to the right. Good enough! He threw on a raincoat over his uniform, and cautiously opened the door of his apartment. Nobody was on the landing. He hurried down the stairs, two at a time, and plunged into the taxi, which started out immediately.

"Anything new on Miss Orchid, Li?"

"No, sir. Everything's just the same."

Miss Orchid was leading a model existence. She went to work early in the morning and came back late at night to the shack where she lived alone. She had no visitors, not even Mr. Pang, who often escorted her home.

"Once a week she goes to the post office and sends a money order to her mother, who lives in a village called Chio-Li-Tsun in Szechwan."

"She must have some friends, some amusements."

"No, sir, not one."

"Where does she take her meals, for instance?"

"When she leaves her shack in the morning she stops at the stand of a certain Mrs. Hu, at the bottom of Diamond Hill, who's one of our informants."

"And at noon, at night?"

"Where she works, I believe. We're there now, sir."

The taxi put MacIntosh down at the entrance to the Asiatic Bank Building on Queen's Road. When the elevator boy saw an American sailor he automatically pressed the button for the seventh floor.

A Cary Grant salute to Mr. Fu of Yang & Co., Tailors.

"Is my suit ready?"

"Certainly, Mr. Johnson. Just a quick fitting. Will you show me your receipt?"

MacIntosh took a wallet out of his hip pocket, spread his various American identification cards on the table, and finally found the receipt in a wad of United States dollars. He handed it to Mr. Fu, who looked it over and then consulted a register.

"Mr. Johnson, we have a great favor to ask you. Your suit was so successful that we sent it as a model to our School of Tailoring in Kowloon. Would you mind trying it on there? Of course we'll pay for a taxi and the ferry. Otherwise I'll call up and have it brought over."

"It's no trouble at all. Delighted to be of service."

"Thank you, Mr. Johnson. You're helping us educate our tailors."

"Don't mention it."

"I'll telephone to say that you're coming."

Mr. Fu picked up the receiver and barked into the mouthpiece: "*Chi Chi wu wu wu* (77555). Pang Hsien Sheng Ah? I'm sending you a customer, Mr. Johnson. For the pin-striped suit, No. 184. A hundred and sixty-five dollars. What's that? Yes, this is Mr. Fu of Yang and Company."

"Odd," MacIntosh thought to himself, "how the most westernized Chinese reverts to type on the telephone. To save face he must be the last to reveal his name."

Mr. Fu hung up and said to him:

"Here's the address. It's 142 Shansi Road, in Kowloon, fourth floor. You'll see a sign on the door, 'Hong Kong School of Tailoring.' Do you know where to take the Kowloon ferry?"

"No, but I'll find it."

"I'll call a taxi, if you like."

"No, I'll get one. Thank you just the same."

"I thank you."

As he went down in the elevator MacIntosh marveled as usual at the prodigious memory of the Chinese. Mr. Fu, who had seen him only once before, when he had come to order the suit, had recognized him immediately and called him by name. And yet he must receive dozens of customers every day. A race of champions!

MacIntosh wondered if, for once, the police had been ill-informed. And yet he had distinctly heard Mr. Fu speak on the telephone to a Mr. Pang. Although there were thousands of Pangs, this seemed to be more than a coincidence. Another sign was the fact that among the other visitors to the Hong Kong School of Tailoring there was not a single civilian, only American sailors.

At first everything seemed to be quite in order. MacIntosh rang the bell and was admitted to a reception room, where he was asked to show the receipt for his suit. Then he was taken to a large room, furnished with long tables, sewing machines, wooden mannequins, steam irons and a blackboard. Pinned to the walls were illustrations of men's fashions. Under the direction of, apparently, the chief tailor, a group of Chinese of all ages were cutting and stitching. Several sailors were trying on their suits in fitting rooms, whose doors were wide open; every now and then one of them came out with a box under his arm. Among the Chinese MacIntosh saw no familiar face. The original Pang Fen-tien, if he had been the one to receive the telephone call, must have embraced an honest trade.

A Chinese, who introduced himself as the head fitter, came forward, followed by two apprentices, with MacIntosh's pin-striped suit over one arm and asked him to try it on. Talking in Shanghai dialect, which MacIntosh found difficult to understand, he seemed to be indicating to the apprentices the points to which every good tailor should give particular attention: the curve of the shoulders, the way the jacket fell in the back.

"It fits you to perfection, sir," he said to MacIntosh. "Just move your arms. Satisfactory? All that's needed is to place the buttons correctly."

He made some chalk marks and handed the jacket over to an apprentice.

"Anyone can see that it comes from Yang and Company, one of the best Hong Kong houses, sir. Only our most promising young men work for them. So far they've done nothing but men's clothes, but soon they're going to go in for feminine fashions as well. We've just opened up a school for dressmakers, right here on the premises. Would you like to see it? We teach feminine styling to men as well, if they want to learn it. Ten Hong Kong dollars a lesson."

"Can I go see it right away?"

"In just a minute, if you don't mind. Here's your jacket. Will you come with me to the cashier while I have your suit folded and put into a box?"

The fitter led MacIntosh back to the reception room, opened a door that MacIntosh had not noticed before, because it was covered with wallpaper, took him through a small empty area, and knocked—four knocks, two by two—at another door, which opened immediately before them. They were in the dressmaking establishment.

At once MacIntosh identified his old friends—Jade Butterfly, Opalescent Moon, Pine Balm, Starry Flower—they were all there, all, that is, except Miss Orchid. They wore short, transparent slips, and each one served as a mannequin for a sailor. The sailors, tape measures (marked off in inches) in hand, obeyed the instructions of a Chinese teacher, measuring the circumference of the neck, the bust, the waist, the hips, then the length of the back, the arms, the legs (inner and outer), and the distance from breast to belly button, and jotting down the figures on a printed blank. Most of the sailors were very slow and had to take the measurements twice. When they had finished, they picked up the boxes containing their suits and went away, and another group followed.

MacIntosh was assigned to Jade Butterfly, a chubby little thing, with broad hips and short legs, the very model of a Chinese woman. She kicked up her legs and giggled when MacIntosh, always meticulous in the performance of duty, expertly tickled her on the front of a very good place indeed.

"*Ni tao yen chi la*" (what a bore!) she protested, in a tone of false indignation.

He was getting ready to tickle her on the reverse side when Miss Orchid entered the room in the same state of undress as the rest. Nervously he finished his lesson with Jade Butterfly and went over to the instructor.

"I haven't really mastered the subject," he said. "Certain details escaped me. Can I have a repeat?"

"Certainly. That will be ten dollars. I see that you're a real student. As a matter of fact, there are a good many like you. Yesterday there was one who took six lessons, one after the other. A gangly boy with pimples; perhaps you know him. Simpson was his name."

"No, I don't know him. Listen, I'd like to change models, in order to broaden my experience."

"Of course. Which one will you have?"

"This young lady," said MacIntosh, pointing to Miss Orchid.

"You have an eye in your head. That's the directress. She knows the technique from top to bottom. With her you'll make fast progress, I'm sure."

He beckoned to Miss Orchid and she came over, saying to him in Chinese that he should leave her alone with this new student. With his heart pounding, but with amazing self-control MacIntosh began to measure her neck.

"*Ni ching cha shih pu shih*" (You're a copper, aren't you?), she said, looking at him with her almond-shaped eyes.

MacIntosh managed not to betray any emotion.

"You police."

"Excuse me. What did you say?"

"You police."

"Me? I'm an American sailor. Look!" And he displayed his papers.

"Last time you come here you no wear glasses. I see you before."

"But this is my first visit to Hong Kong."

"You red hair. I know."

"Me red hair? My hair's black, can't you see?"

"You no police?"

"No. Big ship. Ship with guns. Boom-boom!"

"You work for paper."

"No paper. American sailor."

"You work for paper. Make trouble. No more dress-making school. No more rice to eat."

"No police. No paper. I make no trouble. I like you very much."

Taking advantage of the fact that he was about to slip a tape measure around her waist, he enfolded her in his arms and backed up his statement with a kiss on the ear. She pushed him resolutely away but did not shout or hit him.

"What you want here?"

"To measure you, just like the other sailors."

"No true. I see you before. I see you Lido, with red hair, see you Shoeshine Parlor with red hair, see you Laundry with black hair (pointing to his head and upper lip). Now you wear glasses. What you want?"

"I'm sorry, but you're mistaken, really you are. I like you very much. Do you like me? I'll come back to Hong Kong if you do."

She did not reply, and MacIntosh insisted:

"If you like me, I take you out this evening. Go to the movies. O.K.?"

She looked him straight in the eyes but without speaking, and he wished he could read her thoughts.

"How do you say in Chinese 'I like you'?"

At last she relaxed.

"*Wuo Ai Ni.*"

"*Wuo Ai Ni,*" he stammered, trying to conceal the fact that he knew the language.

An impatient sailor seized the tape measure from MacIntosh's hand.

"Come on, buddy! Aren't you through? It's my turn."

MacIntosh could not answer without betraying his Scottish accent.

"*Wuo,*" he said to Miss Orchid. "Can I see you this evening?"

She looked after him and smiled. At the door he turned and waved his hand, then remembered to give a Cary Grant salute.

"Wealth is like mud; justice is worth its weight in gold."

—CHINESE PROVERB

Chief-Inspector Graham read MacIntosh's latest report attentively.

"Your cover's no good any more, Ian. We can't use you further. Too bad. I'll have to turn the job over to somebody else."

"I don't see why you have to do that, sir. What difference does it make that I've been identified?"

"It makes a lot of difference. What we want to know is whether Pang Fen-tien is running a brothel. As long as he went in for strip-tease acts or petting parties, we overlooked it. But we have strict orders: no prostitution. And if they know you're from the police they aren't going to offer you a girl."

"They're not sure I'm from the police. Miss Orchid took me for a newspaper reporter."

"That's even worse from their point of view. And they'll catch on when no article appears in the papers."

"I'd still like to follow up on the job."

"Well, well! I thought you were fed up with it. Apparently the weekend at Macao did you good. I imagined it would. There's no better cure for chronic bachelorhood."

Graham toyed for a moment with an opium scale, a slender ivory rod with a copper dish suspended by a silk thread at either end, which had been recently seized by the police.

"I've thought it over," said MacIntosh. "I don't like to leave something unfinished."

"O.K. But I can't afford to take any risks. I'll assign Thompson to help you. Let him in on the whole story, and above all don't let him be exposed. Keep him on ice in case Pang Fen-tien starts something new. Until then keep an eye yourself on the dressmaking school. But no more than three suits, one a month, on your expense account! How long do you think the racket will last, anyhow?"

"It's hard to say, sir. They have a good security system of their own. I have an idea that if I hadn't purposely displayed my American identification papers at Yang and Company I'd never have been sent over to the school."

"Yes, but the reporters are hot on the trail. I was at the Correspondents' Club last night, and they were talking of nothing else. Usually they've nothing to do but read the papers from Red China. So that if anything remotely interesting happens at Hong Kong . . ."

"We could always lend a hand to Pang."

"What do you mean?"

"Well, by telling him that the reporters are in the offing."

"Impossible! Can't you see what a stink there'd be if that came out? We can only sit tight and hope that, when the school is closed, Pang will turn his hand to something else."

"That's easy enough to say. But I have an idea he's at the end of his rope."

"Ian, when you know the Chinese as well as I do you'll give more credit to their imagination. If we could allow ourselves the opportunity, there are a few hundred dollar bills to be picked up at the Hong Kong Club at this very moment. Do you know that there are some asses willing to bet that the Chinese won't find any more gimmicks? Just think of the dressmaking school, what a stroke of genius! Tomorrow Pang will invent a school of Chinese medicine, complete with acupuncture and all the rest. Or else . . . or else, I don't know, really."

"By the way, sir, Detective Ho informs us that Pang bought ten bicycles at Kowloon yesterday."

"What for?"

"Just what I'd like to know."

MacIntosh posted himself that very evening at the entrance to the dressmaking school. He had put on his disguise. (The Special Branch had authorized him to keep the uniform as long as necessary.) He waited a long time because they were working late in the workshop while the largest cruiser of the Seventh Fleet was in port.

What always amazed MacIntosh in detective stories was the ease with which the sleuth, disguised as a Pakistani diplomat, kept under cover for hours in front of suspect number one's house in Soho or trailed him through Knightsbridge without ever being spotted. Things seemed to be different in Hong Kong.

A horde of noisy street urchins harassed him for more than an hour: "No papa, no mama, no gasoline! Sooin' gom, sooin' gom!" The Chinese restaurant across the street was "off-limits for American naval personnel," so that he could not take refuge there.

The urchins were followed by a pack of professional beggars who could be recognized by their pitiful grimaces and a display of tactics that closely resembled the submarine strategy of the German wolf packs in the battle of the Atlantic: one beggar would make a sally and when MacIntosh got angry and crossed the street a second one was waiting there to pounce on him.

Then came the guides: "Tailored suits at a bargain price, ready in an hour, cloth guaranteed made in England." Or else: "Genuine ivory balls from the Peking museum, going for nothing, only fifty dollars." One of them had the impudence to propose a "Nice girl, guaranteed virgin." MacIntosh made a mental snapshot of the fellow and vowed to deal with him personally the next day.

He made the mistake of giving a coin to a non-professional woman beggar, recognizable as such because she didn't know any English, and because of a certain dignity in her peasant clothes. The indignant professionals surged upon him from the shadows and he had no choice but to walk around the block.

Three sailors with their clothes boxes rushed out of the school.

"Hey, buddy, where's there a bar around here?"

MacIntosh shrugged his shoulders.

"You don't know? Not very smart, are you? Okay, anyway, c'mon and have a beer with us." MacIntosh shook his head.

"Hey, you got a tongue, ain't you? Or don't you like our mugs?" One of them came at him menacingly. MacIntosh was saved by the guides and the beggars.

About eleven o'clock the lights finally went out on the fourth floor. Orchid left last with Mr. Pang. They went off together in the direction of Nathan Road, where they turned right toward the north of Kowloon. MacIntosh followed them.

Should he go up to Orchid in front of Mr. Pang? "Hi, it's me!" he would say, jovially. "*Wuo,* movie O.K.?" A jeep slowly passing by put an end to his bold resolve: it contained a regular policeman, a British Military Police officer and two sailors from the Shore Patrol. If Miss Orchid or Mr. Pang got it into their heads to make a scene he would be clubbed and taken away before he had time to reel off his name and position. He decided to trail them at a distance in the hope they would split up.

At the end of the gate at Kaytak Airport on the Diamond Hill road the lights were farther apart and the road less frequented at this late hour. MacIntosh still had two limping but fast-moving beggars in his wake, and a tenacious guide. His white uniform was becoming altogether too visible in the darkness. He stopped.

In the distance he saw Miss Orchid and Mr. Pang pause in front of a soup stand. They were brilliantly lit up by a carbide lamp.

A taxi was passing, and MacIntosh hailed it.

The next day he went back to the school, under the pretext of obtaining a slight alteration to his suit, a button to close the inside jacket pocket. He noticed at once that he was the object of particularly deferential attention. Mr. Pang himself took MacIntosh in tow and Miss Orchid, although reserved as ever, gave him another lesson in taking measurements.

Two days later the zipper of his trousers got stuck and had to be replaced. The job was done with alacrity. By now he knew Miss Orchid's measurements by heart, and her courtesy had a purely business character. If only he could find the way to her heart . . .

Soon after this he made up his mind to order a tweed suit, at his own expense. But Yang & Co. was expensive and he chose to go to Feng & Pu, high-class tailors.

Chief-Inspector Graham saw a very excited MacIntosh burst into his office:

"I've got news, Chief-Inspector!"

"Sit down. Some tea?"

"Thanks, sir. Do you remember that the cutting school where I went is at 142 Shansi Road?"

"Yes. Is the tea hot enough?"

"Yes, thanks, sir. Well, yesterday I ordered a suit from another tailor."

"Already? I only authorized you to order one suit a month."

"I know, sir. But it was at my own expense this time. I really did need a sports outfit."

"All right, so?"

"They sent me to try it on in a school on Hankow Road, just behind the Peninsula, at Number sixteen."

Graham scratched his chin a moment. He pressed a bell, which brought the agent Yen.

"Yen, ask Inspector Willis to come and see me immediately." Then to MacIntosh: "Bravo, Ian! The number of the building and the floor?"

Inspector Willis came into the office.

"Willis," said Graham, "get a team ready. To close a camouflaged strip joint in Kowloon."

"Wait a minute, sir. This isn't another joint. It's only a branch of the first one."

"What makes you think so?"

"Simple: they have Miss Orchid, Miss Pine Balm, Miss Precious Treasure . . ."

"You're completely certain it's a branch?"

"Absolutely. I even passed Pang Fen-tien on the stairs." MacIntosh did not specify that Mr. Pang had greeted him with a friendly smile, like an old acquaintance.

Graham grabbed the opium scale and spun it around. "This situation was not foreseen, it creates a problem. One joint, okay; two, no. But if it's a branch . . ."

He put down the scale and lifted the telephone. "Maud? I need to see the boss. Right away? I'm coming.

Wait for me, you two," he said to MacIntosh and Willis. "I'm going to see the Commissioner."

It was a short wait. Back in his office Graham rang for the agent Yen.

"Call Inspector Chao," he told him. "Thanks, Willis, you can run along. I'm taking care of this myself."

XXI

"A short man who knows literature is useful to the kingdom.
A tall man without knowledge, what good is he?"

—CHINESE PROVERB

The night before, Mr. Pang had passed the disguised MacIntosh on the stairs. Early this morning Inspector Chao had come to pay a friendly visit and to say that if Mr. Pang would close the dressmaking school on Hankow Road without delay nothing would give more pleasure to his friends in high places.

Mr. Pang called Miss Orchid: "I'll be away for a few days. I'm leaving the house in your hands."

He bought a jar of Shao Hsing wine and took the bus for Saikung. It was raining when he arrived in the village. Mr. Wu was in his library, painting a flight of cranes in the winter sky. He hummed as he toyed with the paint-brush:

> "In a palace this girl was born,
> So timid, so gracious, so lithe,
> Like a bird in the morning flitting
> Above lotus buds covered with dew.
> If she were mine, this exquisite maiden,
> What would palaces matter to me?"

Mr. Pang filled the cups.

"Very easy, the crane," said Mr. Wu. "A long stroke for the beak, right and left, without lifting the brush off the paper. Now a little circle for the head, like this. You make a very black spot for the eye but only if the crane is close up. Then the neck: two parallel strokes. That isn't hard, is it?"

Mr. Pang filled the cups again.

"You have to be careful here," Mr. Wu resumed. "You have to go on to the feet before drawing the body. There, now."

And he sang:

"Her beauty entrances the guest, but it saddens,
For tomorrow he must go and leave her behind.
She smiles. Where is the gold that would buy such a smile?
What other smiles as she smiles?
No use to cover her body with rarest gems,
But when her dance is over and tender looks exchanged,
Who shall be the one chosen among all the beauties?"

Mr. Wu rubbed his brush on the ink stick. He sighed, "Oh, how I miss that here! If only there were a good opera house in Hong Kong. But the young are no longer interested in it, they prefer the movies. Now look what I do to make the body: a simple triangle, there."

Mr. Pang filled the cups.

"Is it at the movies that they will learn about *The Ruse of the Open City?* Do they know who was the *Desert Cricket?* If you talk to them of *The Chain Plan,* they've never heard of it."

Mr. Wu emptied his cup, and Mr. Pang filled it.

"And yet," Mr. Wu resumed, "what a beautiful story! When I was ten I knew it by heart. Listen:

"One day the usurper Tung Chow held a great banquet. All his officers attended, seated in two long rows. After glasses had been raised a few times, Lü Pu came in and whispered a few words in his father's ear. Chow smiled and said: 'It has always been so. Take Chang Wen outside.' Everyone went pale. A while later a servant brought in the guest's head on a red lacquer plate and showed it to the host. The others nearly died of fright.

"'Have no fear,' said Chow, smiling. 'He was in league

with Yuan Shu to assassinate me. A letter he had written fell accidentally into my son's hands, and I had to eliminate him. But you gentlemen who have nothing for which to reproach yourselves have no need to fear.'

"The officers broke up quickly. One of them, the governor Wang Yun, who had been present at the scene, returned to his home in a pensive and troubled state. It was a beautiful moonlit night and he took his cane and went out to take a walk in his walled garden. Standing near the vine arbor, he looked at the sky and tears coursed down his cheeks. Suddenly there was a noise from the peony pavilion and he head someone sighing. He came up stealthily and saw one of the household singers called Tiao Chan, or Desert Cricket.

"This young woman had been raised in the palace, where she had been taught singing and the dance. She was emerging from adolescence into the full bloom of womanly beauty, an attractive and intelligent girl whom Wang Yun regarded more as a daughter than a servant.

"After listening to her a moment he suddenly cried, 'What sort of scheme are you concocting, evil girl?'

"She knelt in terror: 'Would your miserable servant ever do you any wrong?' she asked.

" 'Then why are you sighing there in the dark?'

" 'May your servant speak from the bottom of her heart?'

" 'Tell me the whole truth, hide nothing from me.'

"And the young girl said, 'Your servant has been showered with your kindness. She has sung and danced and she has been treated with such generosity that if she were torn in pieces for her lord that would not repay him a thousandth part. She has lately noticed that her lord's brow has been furrowed with distress and she knows that it is on account of the troubles in the State. But she dared say nothing. Tonight the lord was more preoccupied than usual and that made her more miserable. But she did not think that she would be seen. Could she be of the slightest use, she would not draw back from a thousand deaths.'

"An idea sprang suddenly to Wang's mind and he struck the ground with his cane. 'Who would have thought that you would hold the destiny of the Hans in the hollow of your hand? Come with me.'

"The young girl followed him to the house. He called together all the women and servants, placed Desert Cricket on a chair, and made a deep bow. She was horrified and threw herself to the ground, anxiously inquiring what the gesture signified.

"He said, 'You may take pity on the fate of the Hans.' And fountains of tears poured forth.

"'I have already told you, you may do with me what you wish, I will not draw back,' said the young girl.

"Wang Yun knelt saying, 'The people are on the edge of destruction, the prince and his officers are in danger, and you, you are the only one who can save them. That bandit Tung Chow seeks to depose the emperor and none of his men can find a way to stop him. He has a son, who it is true is a valiant warrior, but both father and son have a weakness for beauty. I am therefore going to put into operation what I shall call "the chain plan." First I am going to propose your marriage to Lü Pu, and then when you are engaged I will present you to Tung Chow and you will seize every opportunity to divide them, to incite the father to kill his son and thus put an end to our great evils.

Thus will you be able to restore the altars to our land that they may live anew. All this is in your power. Do you consent to do it?' "

Mr. Wu cleared his voice with a mouthful of Shao Hsing and sang:

"Here you are, young girl so beautiful,
Your lips of cherries so red,
Your teeth gleaming like pearls,
Your perfumed breath charged with love.
But your tongue is your sword,
Cold death the recompense
Of your love, o maiden."

Mr. Pang joined him on the last three lines.

"If the rain stops tomorrow," said Mr. Wu, "we'll return to our little island. I'll show you how to paint the wild ducks in the swamp."

"Impossible, dear Mr. Wu, urgent business awaits me in Kowloon; I was only passing by. That will be for another time."

Mr. Pang invited Miss Orchid to dinner in one of the hash houses of Diamond Hill.

"Ah, if only there were a good opera house in Hong Kong! Do you like the opera?"

She had not had the opportunity to go often, for she had spent all her youth in the small village of Chiu Li Tsun. They only had an opera there for the New Year's feast, with traveling singers of very little worth.

"Have you ever heard *The Chain Plan*? That's my favorite," said Mr. Pang.

Miss Orchid had picked up a whole shrimp with her

chopsticks and was busy opening the shell with her teeth. Mr. Pang started singing:

> "Here you are, young girl so beautiful,
> Your lips of cherries so red,
> Your teeth gleaming . . ."

Miss Orchid spat out the shell and said, "If you're looking for a Desert Cricket you're wasting your time with me. I don't like foreigners. In the first place they're hairy as monkeys. Ugh!"

Mr. Pang filled her cup with white wine.

"Bottoms up!" he said.

She gulped down the cupful.

"They may be hairy, but they're said to be very good at making love. They don't need to drink serpent wine or to swallow ground-up rhinoceros horn."

"That's right, real animals! They aren't civilized like us."

"Some women like that."

"Not me."

She held her wine well, too well. Later when he wanted to come into her shack she pushed him resolutely away.

"She whispered, 'I'm not what you think,'" said Detective Li when he made his report to MacIntosh the next day.

Mr. Pang was in his office examining a group of modeling candidates. He studied them rapidly and pointed his pipe at each one. "No . . . No . . . No . . . Yes . . . No."

"What?" roared a candidate's mother, "You wouldn't take my eldest daughter the other time because she didn't have the big bosoms your clients like. Now you refuse to take my second and she's perfect. And that tart you just chose, she's like a flea, now isn't she?"

"Madam," replied Mr. Pang, "I realize that my attitude may seem strange to you. The fact is, we have a difficult client who has special tastes."

Detective Li had told MacIntosh that Mr. Pang's employees were taking bicycle lessons early in the morning over near Diamond Hill. MacIntosh piled his assistant, Thompson, into his red M.G. and went to take a look. Driving at top speed, in order not to be recognized, he very nearly ran down Miss Jade Butterfly, whose balance was to say the least precarious.

As soon as the first month was over MacIntosh lost no time in ordering a gray flannel suit from Yang & Co. Mr. Pang came to meet him at the door of the school, and Miss Orchid was prodigal with her attentions.

"How happy I am to see you again, Mr. Johnson!" Mr. Pang exclaimed. "Miss Orchid and I were wondering when your honorable ship would put in at Hong Kong. I trust the sea hasn't been too rough."

"A few squalls near Okinawa. But nothing terrible."

"We have a new model, just the kind for you. A girl of very good family, who had to divorce her hard-drinking husband because he beat her."

And he added, turning to Miss Orchid:

"Bring on Miss Desert Cricket. An unusually able dressmaker, you'll see that for yourself, Mr. Johnson. And she speaks English as well as you and I."

Escorted by a beaming Miss Orchid, Miss Desert Cricket came across the room. Her hair was waved and dyed a mahogany color, and she walked like Marilyn

Monroe, minus the more obvious points of the figure. She was smoking a cigarette in a long black holder.

"How do you do, Mr. Johnson," she said, batting her eyelashes.

MacIntosh gave a feeble Cary Grant salute.

"I hope you're spending several days at Hong Kong," she went on. "It's such a provincial town that we're always glad to see friends from abroad."

"We'll leave you to your lesson," said Mr. Pang, clapping MacIntosh cordially on the shoulder. "Take care of Miss Desert Cricket's chest measurements. That's the crucial part of the lesson. You'll instruct him carefully, won't you, Miss Cricket? I'm counting on you."

Mr. Pang and Miss Orchid walked away, not without looking over their shoulders. From a distance they turned around to scrutinize the pupil and his new teacher, then they went out through an inside door. It was only after several minutes had gone by that MacIntosh recovered his professional curiosity.

"Miss, ah . . . Desert Cricket, do you live in Kowloon?"

"Certainly, Mr. Johnson; I have a little studio in Hankow Road at number sixteen."

"And . . . you live alone?"

"Alone, alas."

"You're not afraid?"

"A little. A lady alone in the streets is always exposed to stupid remarks."

"And what do you do in the evening?"

"I go back home and read."

"Would you be free for dinner tonight?"

"I should very much like to go out with you, but unfortunately I am not allowed to. We are forbidden to go out with the clients when an American ship is in port. Otherwise it would be a pleasure."

"Who makes that stupid rule?"

"It is Mr. Pang, our honorable director. No, I beg you, Mr. Johnson, don't kiss me, Mr. Pang doesn't like that. Come on, be good, Mr. Johnson, please, please . . ."

XXII

"The past is as clear as a mirror;
The future is dark as a varnish."

—CHINESE PROVERB

MacIntosh had acquired both a summer and a winter wardrobe at the Queen's expense by the time Chief-Inspector Graham summoned him to his office one morning.

"Have you read the *Chronicle?*" he fired point-blank at his faithful subordinate.

"Yes, sir. Too bad! But this time Pang has beaten his record. It took the newspaper chaps four months to find him out."

"And he's had four months to hatch his new plan."

"What do you mean, sir?"

"Inspector Chao found the school closed this morning. Pang closed it on his own initiative. But take Thompson with you and go have a look over at Kaytak. You'll find something to interest you."

REPORT

by Inspector Jack Thompson, first flying squad of the Royal Hong Kong Police Force
Re: Bicycle Taxis.
Follow-up of verbal instructions from Chief Inspector Graham of the R.H.K.P.F.

1. Today, 28 June, 1953, in the disguise of an American sailor, I took the bus to Kaytak. In it were a dozen other sailors. We got out at the end of the line and walked together for two miles along the road coming down from Kowloon Peak.

2. For the last mile, all the way to the hairpin bend, both sides of the road were crowded with Chinese urchins from Diamond Hill, a certain number of adults, and some sailors carrying cameras. Four uniformed policemen were striving to maintain order and to keep the road open. The general atmosphere was that of a carnival.

3. At a certain point there was a loud noise higher up on the road, which came down gradually toward us. A bicycle, ridden by a Chinese girl, with an American sailor mounted behind her, was speeding down the slope at about twenty-five miles an hour. The onlookers applauded, the sailors snapped and filmed pictures, and the policemen busied themselves stopping any trucks that attempted to circulate on the road. This scene was repeated several times over as we started uphill. Soon we overtook a young cyclist whom I recognized as Miss Orchid (cf. preceding reports by Inspector MacIntosh). She was climbing up the hill on foot, pushing her bicycle. One of the sailors in my group stepped up and offered to pedal the bicycle as far as the bend.

4. Here there was a group of Chinese, among them Pang Fen-tien, and some other sailors, who were waiting for their turn. The price of a ride down the hill was 10 Hong Kong dollars, payable in advance.

5. I took a ride myself, behind Miss Pine Balm. The general idea back of this mode of transportation is essentially sound. The passenger, seated on a baggage rack with a cushion on top of it, is obliged to cling to the rider, preferably by winding his arms around her chest and holding very tight. The configuration of the road and the lack of traffic make the site well chosen.

6. However, the enterprise has certain disadvantages.

a) Judging from my own reactions, although the passenger at first quite enjoys squeezing the rider his enjoyment soon changes to fear and he clutches her with unexpected violence. I heard some of the sailors, when they got to the bottom, ask for a "congressional medal of honor." Accustomed as they are to maneuvers of a high technical precision, they didn't seem to enjoy the dangers of this headlong, zigzag race down the hill with such ill-trained pilots in the saddle. One of them, apparently a flyer, said it reminded him of the day when he was in a jet that landed on its carrier in the midst of a typhoon. In my opinion, once the novelty of the sport has worn off, it will attract only a few breakneck adventurers.

b) Only ten bicycles are in use. The downward trip requires only a few breath-taking minutes, but the climb up, on foot, occupies a full quarter of an hour. Much of the time, then, is unproductive.

c) Some of the sailors complained that the girls didn't have "what it takes in the right places." Especially a pimply youth called Simpson. Miss Pine Balm suited me very well, but I heard a number of complaints about Miss Orchid. Her passengers went so far as to try to get back their money. Mr. Pang obliged them and withdrew Miss Orchid from the riders.

d) I watched the goings-on for about two hours. Only three sailors asked for a second ride, and that apparently just in order to win bets they had made with their friends.

7. A couple of carloads of reporters arrived around eleven o'clock. Among them were two newsreel cameramen. They had a long pow-wow

with Mr. Pang, who finally allowed one of them to have a ride, after stating that his transportation service was run for the exclusive use of the United States Navy and insisting that the cameraman sign a declaration that he was taking the ride at his own risk.

8. I had to leave, for fear that one of the reporters, George Bennett, whom I have met around town, might recognize me. Until the time of my departure I saw no accident or other unpleasantness. Detective Li, who was among the onlookers from eight o'clock in the morning to four in the afternoon, telephoned me later to say that nothing out of order had happened. He told me that Miss Orchid, apparently rigged out in some sort of padding, had rejoined the bicycle riders, and that there were no more complaints about her; in fact, her clients seemed to be delighted.

Signed: J. Thompson.

"What do you say, Ian," asked Chief-Inspector Graham.

"I was right," said MacIntosh. "Pang is at the end of his rope."

"I don't agree. He has a trick or two up his sleeve, you can be sure of that."

"But this latest enterprise is completely impractical."

"How many Chinese do you know who are impractical? There must be some reason behind it."

"I can't see it."

"Just stop to think. I can see at least one. If you don't find it in a week, you will owe me a bottle of gin. By the way, check with the traffic department to see if all this bicycling is a real nuisance. Tell them that we are inclined to let him go on with it. The only thing is that the rick-shaw men may complain of the competition, and if Pang hasn't a license they can have him put out of business. Send Inspector Chao to hint to him he'd better get one, and then tell them at Kowloon to satisfy his request."

"Yes, sir."

"And one more thing, Ian. The boss agrees that you're to take the place of Chief-Inspector Barnes in two months. When the time comes you must celebrate. But meanwhile get going."

Assistant Commissioner Ferguson had risen in rank while continually holding the post of Chief of the Traffic Division of the Hong Kong police. Fifteen years before he had started simply as an inspector. It is true that there were not so many cars in those days.

When he is asked what was the most memorable day of his life he unhesitatingly replies, "June 30, 1953."

It was just an ordinary Sunday. There was no political occasion on the calendar that day, and no sporting or cultural event, except for the annual outing of the Amateur Photographers, who occupied no more than twenty or thirty extra vehicles. That did not call for an added traffic detail.

It was a normal Sunday, the kind when British subjects can be fitted into four main categories according to well-established statistics:

1. The Sporting Type: gets up early, has a light breakfast, jumps into the car, and drives either to the Royal Hong Kong Golf Club at Fanling, near the Chinese border, or else to the Royal Yacht Club, at the port, where

races start. The hours traffic is affected are 7 to 8 a.m. and 7 to 10 p.m.

2. The Family Man who has his children with him in the Colony: gets up at a reasonable hour, piles the whole household in the car, including the boy, and goes for a picnic either in the car or on a boat. Traffic going all morning; return traffic at nightfall.

3. The Young Bachelor: sleeps late, particularly if he's been at the Correspondents' Club the night before, collects his friends from 3 p.m. on, and goes to one of the beaches. Traffic hours, 3–4 p.m., 6–7 p.m.

4. Others: rise both early and late, go to church, are comfortably bored for the rest of the day, alone or with guests. Traffic hours—see schedule of religious services.

It was a Sunday in which the Chinese with cars also fell into two basic categories:

1. Those who observe the Sabbath (the minority): cram family and relations (eleven people at minimum) into their little Austins and go for a ride around the New Territories. Especially dangerous traffic hour: 5 to 6 p.m.

2. Those who do not observe the Sabbath: they attend to their usual occupations, which no one has ever been able to catalogue.

Ferguson, who was at this time an inspector discharging the function of Chief-Inspector, was having a late sleep in his studio apartment at Victoria Mansion on the Peak. The first sign of trouble came when the telephone rang persistently on the bedside table.

"Sir?" It was Thomas, his assistant on duty that Sunday.

"Yes, Thomas. What time is it?"

"Ten-twenty. Very sorry to wake you, sir, but I've been

informed of a terrible jam at the car ferry on the Hong Kong side. The ferry boat company has doubled its service, but more than six hundred cars are waiting to cross."

"What's happening? Have you any idea?"

"The Kowloon police have radioed just now about a huge crowd of pedestrians heading for Kaytak."

"Are they Chinese?"

"Yes, of course."

"I don't get the connection."

"Nor do I, sir. Chinese crowds and European cars only come together at Happy Valley on the Saturdays when there are races. But this is Sunday, and in any case the race track is on the island side."

"Right you are. Maybe the good weather is bringing more people out this morning. Is it very pleasant?"

"Superb."

"That's what it is then. Don't worry, Thomas. They'll be jammed for the next hour or two. Do your best, old boy, I'm counting on you."

As he was temporarily wakened, Ferguson asked the boy for a cup of strong tea without cream or sugar. He would be glad of it later. He drank it and went back to sleep.

Not for long. The telephone rang again about eleven. Ferguson held the receiver at arm's length and at once heard a nasal roar.

"Ferguson?"

It was the voice of Commissioner Osbourne, Chief of District One (Central Hong Kong). The line had transmitted with surprising high fidelity an unmistakable tone of rage:

"What the devil are you doing? There has never been

such a jam in Hong Kong and you're sleeping. Pleasant dreams, I hope. It's a damned disgrace, and your division is the worst of all."

"But, but . . ."

"The boss has been blocked in his car for an hour between the Peak and downtown, and I warn you he's not in a good humor. He's given me a real rating—you'll pay for that, my friend."

"How could he if he's stuck in his car?"

"His radio, you . . . you . . ."

"I'm going right away."

"I strongly advise it!"

Ferguson cut himself three times shaving, fastened his shoulder-belt on the run, and rushed to his car. It did not get far. At the turn at Wong Nei Chong where the Peak road crosses the top, cars were lined up bumper to bumper. A symphony of horns was coming from the city below, which indicated an extreme impatience on the part of the usually self-controlled British drivers.

Ferguson abandoned his Austin and went down the highway on foot, quickly but without rushing, as became an official of Her Majesty in uniform who must show by his attitude in a state of crisis that there is nothing to get excited about, that the mix-up will soon be straightened out and normalcy restored.

In the distance he recognized the Chief Commissioner's Humber caught between a taxi and a Chevrolet. The C.C. was dressed in civilian clothes, sitting in the back seat reading the *Hong Kong Chronicle*. Ferguson was sure that with a bit of luck he could get by without being seen. But his professional training was stronger than his instincts. With his stomach in knots he came up, clicked his heels and accompanied his salute with a resounding "Sir!"

The C.C. was charm itself.

"Remarkable day, don't you think, Ferguson?"

"Sir! I don't really understand what could have happened."

"I was thinking just that myself. This has never happened before. Just imagine, I've been in my car for over an hour in the full heat of the sun without perspiring. You must admit that's remarkable!"

"I'm sincerely sorry, sir."

"Don't distress yourself, it's not your fault, my friend. Come along to the G.Q. We'll both see what can be done."

The C.C. was in a confidential mood. On the way he said to Ferguson: "Have you any idea what caused all this?"

"Absolutely none, sir. There was nothing exceptional on the calendar, I made sure myself yesterday."

"I'm certain of it. Do you know about the bicycle taxis around Kaytak?"

"Yes, sir. Inspector MacIntosh spoke to me about them just yesterday. He wanted to know if I thought they'd block local traffic."

"And what did you answer?"

"That I didn't see how they could cause much trouble. A few bicycles on a highway that only trucks use, that's no problem."

"You couldn't have guessed, I suppose. Nor could I. There's the direct cause of this jam, those few bicycles of yours."

"Sir, I beg your pardon!"

"All these people want to see the American sailors come down Kowloon Peak on a bicycle behind a Chinese girl."

"I'm frightfully sorry, sir."

"Don't get upset, it's not your fault. You're only a victim of power politics, I guess."

"I beg your pardon, sir?"

"It's a bit complicated to explain to you. It's a matter that touches directly on the security of the Colony, its economy and even on world strategy and our relations with the Americans."

"Is that so, sir?"

The Chief Commissioner did not reply right away. They were now at the level of Government House. He pointed at the official buildings and said: "When we presented them with the report on the bicycle taxis yesterday, someone very highly placed there wrote in the margin: 'An enterprise of an essentially sporting nature that could not be of harm to the Colony.'"

The situation got back to normal about one o'clock in the morning. The next day the bar of the Hong Kong Club was short on gin and tonic. Neither gin nor tonic nor ice could be had after six-thirty. It was the first such scandalous incident since the Club was founded. Colonel Gwynn stood in line like everyone else in front of the secretary's office, and wrote in the complaints book:

"There will be a formal investigation unless the drinks committee resigns immediately."

XXIII

"Without urbanity there is neither virtue nor justice."

—CHINESE PROVERB

A certain high-placed official felt rather small after these catastrophic events. His first concern was to study the reaction in the Communist camp, for surely the Sunday traffic jam and the reasons for it would not have passed unnoticed by its agents. He searched the daily bulletin of the New China Agency in vain. He had the *Ta Kung Pao* translated from the headlines to the last page without finding a word about it. For conscience's sake he asked Leslie Barrington-Jones to send an inquiry to Her Majesty's Chargé d'Affaires at Peking. There was nothing to report. He breathed easier without trying to figure things out.

The official was careful not to put in an appearance at the Hong Kong Club despite the heat and his own thirst. The remarks about his absence were all the more biting since he had been very active on the drinks committee, having insisted particularly on trying out the American concoction, whiskey sour.

His voluntary exile was mercifully short, as another sensational event drew attention from his disgraceful slackness. However, let us return to Mr. Pang.

Mr. Pang had also had a scare. For a few days the mere sight of a policeman was enough to threaten him with heart failure. He was sure they would extradite him. However, the police were only coming to keep traffic moving on Kowloon Peak, keep the spectators in order, prevent children from getting run over by the bicycles, and stop the trucks when necessary. The police had been obliging enough to station an ambulance at the foot of the slope. This was somewhat depressing to the clients, so Mr. Pang requested the nurse to park the ambulance in a more discreet location.

So much concern was reassuring to Mr. Pang. To prove that he was not ungrateful, he sent a check for a thousand dollars to the secretary of the Charitable Association of the Royal Police of Hong Kong.

Inspector MacIntosh was at a loss over the phenomenal success of the bicycle taxis. His forecasts had been proved completely wrong. He willingly admitted to his chief, Graham, "It's a profitable enterprise after all."

"Don't you change your mind a bit quickly?"

"I went there with Thompson this morning. He can confirm it for you: at least two hundred sailors were waiting in line. At ten dollars a head, count it for yourself."

"In that case why doesn't Pang buy more bicycles? Do you know of any Chinese who aren't interested in expanding their businesses?"

"He has to find girls to ride them."

"If he wanted a hundred girls in an hour, he could find a thousand."

"So what's the reason?"

"I'll clue you in, my dear Ian. How many newspapermen did you see there this morning?"

"Three. They were just passing through, according to Jack, who knows them all here."

"And you still can't guess?"

"No, chief, I'm sorry to be so slow."

"Don't you see that Pang is using a diversionary tactic? It's in front of your nose! On the first day the newspapermen rush over, it's a sensation, great copy. By the third day it's routine, no one bothers any more and your friend Pang is finally left in peace. You'll see if I'm not right. But not a word of this to anyone, it's between you and me."

Graham turned out to be right. After the third day the newspaper reporters let the bicycle taxis alone. They had some shock value, but as a steady diet they were of no interest. Soon the onlookers, too, faded away, at least the adults among them. The street urchins continued to hang around in the hope that the American sailors would give them chewing gum and candy. But the sailors themselves came in diminishing numbers. Mr. Pang had to make exceptions to his rule and accept the money of civilian sensation-seekers.

When news reached the Hong Kong Club that the enterprise was hanging by a hair, some of Mr. Pang's most faithful supporters—Colonel Gwynn, Mr. Crabb, Mr. Lewys and Leslie Barrington-Jones—resolved to give up their usual Sunday sports and go to the rescue. Bobo, who had to entertain a visiting French admiral, apparently sent solely to interfere with his regular game of golf, decided to bring him along.

Mr. Pang's adversaries, the upholders of a tough policy, put in an appearance too, led by Mr. Chase and Mr. Baron. Their applause was ironical, for the taste of victory was in their mouths. They had wagered four thousand dollars that this ridiculous bicycle-taxi racket wouldn't last longer than a month and now the prospect of victory was making up for all their defeats of the period before. Hitler, too, had won every battle, but he had lost the war.

Mr. Crabb, as a member of the Yacht Club's racing committee, had the theoretically sound idea of setting up regular competitions, complete with rules, handicaps and judges. But the enthusiasm aroused by his efforts was purely artificial; it was obvious that all genuine interest had faded away.

In the car that took them back to the city Mr. Crabb and Mr. Lewys were taciturn and Colonel Gwynn was lost in thought.

"Arthur!" he called out abruptly as Mr. Crabb was driving up the ramp to the ferry. "We're saved! Lieutenant-Colonel Arthur, the commando leader, was under me when he first came out of Sandhurst. He's permanently in my debt."

"Colonel, please explain."

"His commando numbers ninety men. Suppose he sends them to ride the bicycle taxis twice a week. Isn't that the perfect daredevil training? What do you say?"

The silence with which this idea was received was ominous.

"Very fine in principle," Mr. Crabb said mournfully. "But after my three war years in the Quartermaster's Corps I doubt that the Army will come up with ten dollars an hour for daredeviltry. Only the Americans would throw around that much money. And they're getting their training free, in Korea. Let's have a G.T."

The next week was a black one, for no ships of the United States Navy put in at Hong Kong. Did this signify displeasure or merely a stepping-up of operations in Korea? To his surprise Bobo was unable to get any explanation out of the usually loquacious American naval attaché. Peterson, the economist, was really pathetic. At the regular Wednesday meeting he sat hunched up in his chair with a tragic air. When H. E. asked him about the economic picture he made a gesture like that used to describe the descent of a dive bomber. H. E., as usual, nodded.

Mr. Pang, however, continued to hang on.

When Inspector Chao tried to sound out his intentions he was told that the idea of the bicycle taxis was fundamentally sound, even if slow to develop, and that he had no intention of giving it up. What, he asked, were the feelings of Mr. Chao's superiors? They were not enthusiastic, the inspector told him, but there was nothing to fear. The business was perfectly legal and there was no plan to forbid it. Nevertheless . . .

"Nevertheless?" asked Mr. Pang.

"Nevertheless . . ." Inspector Chao repeated, starting to get up.

"Does Inspector Chao care for sea bathing?"

"Certainly, when I have time. Why do you ask?"

"If the Inspector has time tomorrow, I should like to take him to the shore."

And so Mr. Pang drove Inspector Chao to Clear Water Bay. Also in the car were the Misses Orchid, Starry Flower, Springtime Harmony, Opalescent Moon, Pine Balm, Jade Butterfly, Precious Treasure and Desert Cricket, besides the boy Ah Hing, eleven persons in all.

With the aid of Officer Yen, Chief-Inspector Graham was packing his files in cardboard boxes. Police headquarters was moving out of its shabby old quarters into a brand-new building on a piece of newly drained land beyond the naval base. The move had been painstakingly prepared and Graham had only an hour for the transfer of his own office. Just at this moment Detective Li knocked at his door.

"Is it urgent, Li?"

"I'm not too sure."

"Well, what is it?"

"Pang Fen-tien is negotiating for the purchase of two junks at Shau Kiwan."

"Are you sure?"

At once Graham regretted the futility of this question.

"Yen, go find MacIntosh and Thompson. I don't give a hang about moving. Hurry!"

MacIntosh and Thompson were busy with their own moving, but they dropped everything to obey the summons.

"Pang is buying two junks," Graham told them. "I always said that the bicycle taxis were just a smokescreen. Follow up closely on this new enterprise. I don't believe for a minute that Pang is turning into a yachtsman."

At Government House the news created quite a ripple. Things had come almost to the point of asking the Americans for an official explanation of the absence of their ships from Hong Kong. Luckily Leslie was able to tear up the telegram he had just written to this effect to the Foreign Office and rushed over to see Peterson.

There was still considerable tension when, on July 20, 1953, MacIntosh showed Graham the photographs he had taken from a police launch. Graham sent these, by messenger, to Government House, where they were examined under a magnifying glass by Leslie, the Honorable Secretary and His Excellency in person. His Excellency's aide-de-camp noticed that the raised eyebrows of the three betrayed their emotion. When His Excellency gave him the photographs to put away and he was at last able to examine them, he understood the reason.

"My friends," Graham said to his subordinates. "I want reports for tomorrow. Each of you will take one of the junks. And if you're spotted, Ian, so much the worse. You are to act quite separately."

In view of the urgency of the situation it had been decided to have the two inspectors in their disguise as sailors make a report immediately.

"Fantastic, sir!"

"Don't tell me a thing yet; the C.C. is waiting for us. You haven't seen Thompson?"

"No."

"He'll join us; let's go."

It was the first time MacIntosh had been in the Chief Commissioner's office. Maud, the secretary, who had let them in, sat down at the end of the table, ready to record. MacIntosh barely had time to admire the huge relief map of the Colony taking up the whole wall behind the C.C.

"I'm listening, Inspector."

"Yes, sir. I put on this outfit this morning on the Chief-Inspector's orders and went to Shau Kiwan in a taxi driven by Detective Li. I had him drop me on the typhoon shelter docks and started mixing with a group of American sailors. We set off shortly on one of the sampans that are used as ferries between the docks and two junks anchored five hundred yards east of the point of Shau Kiwan."

"Just a second, please. What American sailors? As far as I know there's no ship on visit."

"They belong to the transport crew that is here permanently, sir."

"True, I didn't think of that. Thank God for transport. Continue."

"The junks are anchored out of sight of the docks. The sampan transported us to the junk named Hai Feng, the Sea Breeze in English."

"Thanks for the translation. Will you have some tea?"

Maud served them. MacIntosh waited until she had sat down to continue his account.

"This junk carries registration number 457. She must weigh five tons."

"Are you by chance accustomed to gauging the tonnage of junks?"

"No, sir."

"Because one can sometimes double the real weight in guessing at it. But that's a detail. Go on."

"Aboard the junk there was a crew consisting of two sailors, a cabin boy and the captain. There were also five Chinese girls in bikinis. One of these, Miss Springtime Harmony . . . I don't know whether you know her . . ."

"No, I don't . . ."

"She asked us for twenty Hong Kong dollars. There were ten of us sailors. We got undressed in the main cabin and came back up on deck in our bathing trunks. One American sailor who had none stayed in his shorts. Miss Springtime Harmony split us up in two groups and we proceeded to give individual swimming lessons to the girls."

"Did they have waterwings?"

"No, sir."

"The water was over your heads, though . . ."

"Oh, but they know how to swim. Now I know why Pang Fen-tien was taking them to Clear Water Bay. The lesson lasted for ten minutes. The captain of the junk blew a whistle and we all climbed back aboard . . ."

MacIntosh paused, as someone knocked. Maud opened the door and let Thompson in. He took several parade steps, clicked his heels and saluted in regulation style. His British stiffness appeared so absurd coupled with his sailor disguise that everybody burst out laughing. It took Jack some time to get the joke, and then he joined in the general hilarity.

"Continue, MacIntosh," the C.C. said finally.

"I was saying that we got back on board when the whistle blew. Then they offered us a few extra features. For two more dollars we had the privilege of drying off the girls with small towels. For ten dollars we were allowed to be present in the cabin where the girls put on their clothes. Oh, I forgot: the sailors could film the swimming lesson for a fee of five dollars."

"How much did it cost you in all?"

"Twenty-two dollars because I didn't take pictures, plus two dollars for the sampan."

"Don't you find that a bit steep, Graham?" asked the C.C. "I have an idea Pang is going too far."

"It's hard to put a price on pleasure. If the Americans complain and if Pang doesn't lower his prices we can always intervene."

"You're right. Now MacIntosh, did anything else go on? You get my meaning."

"Yes, sir. While the Chinese girls were changing in the cabin, one sailor tried to take advantage of the situation to kiss one of them. She protested, and the other sailors threw him overboard with all his clothes on. When I tried to follow his example I got the same treatment. That meant I had to stay on board for a second show waiting for my clothes to dry."

"That's all?"

"Yes, sir."

"Your turn, Thompson."

"My sampan took me to the other junk, whose registered number is 2145 and whose name has two Chinese characters that I was unable to decipher. Aboard the junk I found Pang Feng-tien, Miss Orchid, Miss Opalescent Moon, Miss Pine Balm, Miss Starry Flower—that is, the whole gang. They were all wearing bikinis. One of them was a real come-on, you should have seen her—a girl called Desert Cricket. I'd already noticed her in the bicycle-taxi team, but today was the first time I'd seen her in the nude, or almost. I had thought she was rather flat-chested, but was she—um, stacked! We had to restrain two fellows who were trying to get at her."

"Maud, if you please, tea for Inspector Thompson. Go on, Thompson."

"Yes, sir. This is how it went. Pang Fen-tien clapped his hands and a girl jumped overboard and pretended to be drowning. A visitor was chosen to undress quickly and dive in to rescue her. He played with her a little in the water, a standard part of the arrangement, and brought her back up on deck. There he practiced artificial respiration on her. There is a choice between the classical method, which costs ten dollars, and the modern one for twenty."

"Elucidate, please."

"For the classical method the patient lies on her stomach and the practitioner straddles her lower back and presses her ribs rhythmically. It's exhilarating, but not as much as the other, the 'mouth to mouth' method. I tried the classical with Miss Pine Balm and the modern with Miss Orchid. Do you know how the 'mouth to mouth' is done, sir?"

"I can guess. Proceed."

"You can film it for five dollars. What else can I tell you? . . ."

"There was no incident on your junk?"

"Oh, yes, I was going to speak of it. Naturally this life-saving has a very stirring effect, whichever method is used. Each time I had to take a long bath in order to cool off, and the water actually seemed warm. I must say that the American sailors impressed me. They must be very well trained despite appearances, because they displayed a self-control of which I'd never thought them capable. They cooled themselves off like me, but I still think we've got to take care, sir. These sailors are stationed at Hong Kong and can satisfy their needs in the city, but when the others are called back from Korea or elsewhere, I'm afraid of a ruckus. Pang Fen-tien has only two Chinese sailors with him, and they'll never be able to stand up to Yankees six feet tall. If I may be permitted to make a suggestion, it wouldn't be a bad idea to have a police launch assigned to patrol duty near the junks."

"Quite so. Anything else?"

"Yes, one other thing. Desert Cricket, her, um, her breasts were made of rubber. We found out while they were practicing the classical method on her. They didn't hold up under the weight of the bruiser who was straddling her. He began to complain. You should have seen his face when the fellow he'd nearly had a fight with started sniggering at him. That should have been on film! I took a film, by the way, sir, if you want to see . . ."

"Excellent, Thompson. You, too, MacIntosh. Maud, you've got all that down, no questions?"

"No, sir," she replied, blushing.

"Very good. Carry on, then. Leave me with the Chief-Inspector."

Thompson had begun to execute the British regulation salute when he changed his mind and finished it in the easy-going manner of American sailors. Since he didn't quite know how he should salute, MacIntosh left in confusion, giving a Cary Grant.

"There you are," the C.C. sighed. "Things have reached just the point I feared. Good heavens, Graham, I forgot: remind Thompson to leave his film."

Graham dashed out and returned shortly with exhibit A.

"It's more than strip tease, it's more than 'petting,' as they call it."

"It's really going too far."

"Government House will have to decide. The moment it's a matter of power politics, you understand . . ."

"Thompson is right, sir, we're sure to run into trouble."

"We'll carry out the orders. As soon as Maud has typed the report I'll send it to them with the film. They'll decide."

"There is, perhaps, one solution, sir. I don't know how good it is . . ."

"Tell us your idea, anyway."

"If we asked the Americans to send their ships here only after putting in to Japan for a few days, don't you think their men would be quieter?"

"Not bad. We can always try. I'll speak to H. E. about it. About MacIntosh, he will replace Barnes in eight days. You can tell him so."

MacIntosh and Thompson waited for Graham in his office.

"Jack, I advise you to spend the weekend studying Chinese at Macao," Graham said to Thompson by way of dismissal.

"Thank you very much, chief, but I have all I want right here. If you don't need me any longer I'll be off. If you could have seen me with Miss Orchid: A volcano, that's what she is, and as ticklish as a kitten."

MacIntosh shot his colleague a black look.

"One minute, Jack!" said Graham. "You're not chasing any of Pang's girls, I hope."

"Certainly not, chief, the service and all that, can't mix the two."

"Right. Good luck, then."

During the next two weeks a 45,000-ton aircraft carrier, two cruisers, one of them the flagship, a group of transports, a submarine supply ship and two flotillas of destroyers all anchored at Hong Kong while a dozen four-engine DC-4's of the United States Air Force made an air lift between Japan and Kaytak.

Government House felt that the aquatic games organized by Mr. Pang had an educational and humanitarian value, and that they were well this side of the line.

Prosperity caused Mr. Pang to rent two more junks, which he added to his fleet. His employees had acquired a tan that lent considerable zest to the undressing.

MacIntosh had bought from the big Hong Kong store Lane, Crawford a special bikini imported from California. The upper part, made of rubber, served a double purpose as a girdle and a life preserver. He sent it anonymously to Miss Orchid. The bathing suit was very becoming, which perhaps suggests that he had not forgotten what he had learned at the dressmaking school. Now, to his great relief, he noticed that Miss Orchid had abandoned the mouth to mouth method of artificial respiration in favor of the classical system.

The bicycle taxis continued on their slalom course down Kowloon Peak. Their activities were very reassuring to the members of the Correspondents' Club.

XXIV

"When a man is subtle, no explanations are necessary; when the skin is drawn tight over a drum, it need not be beaten twice."

—CHINESE PROVERB

Mr. Pang had given himself considerable pains for very little with his bicycle taxi business. He could not have imagined that Providence would come to his aid, even if he did deserve it. For Providence it was that created the diversion of which he stood so sorely in need.

In August 1953 a certain Dr. San was accused of having taken advantage of a twenty-two-year-old working girl refugee, Miss Ts'ui, who happened to be a virgin. Well-informed people were sure he had engaged in activities that, although pleasurable, were not in accordance with the Hippocratic Oath. Was it rape? It was complex. The details were discussed over the bar of the Hong Kong Club, and it was whispered in the reading room that the affair had been engineered by the doctor's permanent procuress. It was a classic case of refined vengeance in the Chinese manner. The customer had been more assiduous about obtaining the goods than about paying for them. The odds on the doctor's acquittal were three to two, and Mr. Crabb, in his role of amateur bookmaker, had a hard time keeping track of all the bets.

The machinery of Her Majesty's justice began to move and in due course set up a public inquiry to determine whether or not there had been a crime.

Although British newspapers are liable to heavy sanctions if they print any stories before a trial is held, they are free to give fully detailed accounts of the proceedings once it has taken place. And in a case like this the details are necessarily prurient, which is to say appealing from the journalistic point of view.

The defense claimed that their client had merely examined the patient (previously rendered drowsy by an injection) with the instrument necessary for the purpose. The prosecution affirmed that said instrument, although solid, was not made of metal. Much, apparently, hinged on the question of initial temperature.

The accusation was too serious for the bewigged crown judge to dispense with cross-examination and the full legal procedure of a trial. The delighted press wrung a number of special editions from the case.

Mr. Pang, who followed the case attentively, was not slow in concluding that his affairs would be pushed out of the news for at least six months, since the public inquiry was sure to be followed by an equally public trial. With a little luck one of the parties involved would appeal the case. In any event he prudently kept the bicycle taxis in operation.

Yes, Mr. Pang had every reason to be pleased. Although he had been born in the seaside city of Tsingtao and was a former employee of the United States Navy, Mr. Pang was not a good sailor. Aboard the junks he was perfectly miserable. For some obscure reason the waters of the bay of Hong Kong are always rough and toss small boats about, even when the open sea is calm. The swimming lessons based on the *Hai Feng* and the life-saving course based on the *Yun Lung* (Lucky Dragon) were extremely profitable, but they required his presence every day. It was impossible to delegate to the capable Miss Orchid the responsibility for keeping discipline aboard. And a male lieutenant who would not be tempted, for a financial consideration, to wink at the liberties that some of the girls might allow the sailors was not easy to find.

An armistice in Korea was in the offing because of the Five-Year Plan of the Kung Chang Tang (Communist Party), Mr. Han, the banker, had informed him. Would this put an end to the visits of American ships to Hong

Kong? No, said Mr. Han. The Eisenhower government would be mistrustful of the Communists and leave part of the Seventh Fleet on guard for some months to come. Indochina and Formosa were still danger points.

One morning in September when the water was especially rough, Mr. Pang, who had read in the *Chronicle* that an early typhoon was building up from the direction of Guam, decided that the situation called for action, and he took off on the first available sampan. Without bothering to go back to his house he took the Saikung bus. He found Mr. Wu busy overseeing the construction of a pavilion in his garden.

"It's for painting crabs and shrimps. No one will bother me here," said Mr. Wu. He was sorry, he added that, as he hadn't expected Mr. Pang's visit, he had planned to inspect his corset factory at Kowloon this afternoon where some new machines were being installed. Would Mr. Pang perhaps care to accompany him?

The factory had the look of a construction site. In the yard, between concrete-mixers and cranes that were carefully lifting the new machines to the second floor of a brand-new building, a dozen coolies like busy ants were loading cases onto trucks while others were writing their destinations on them: Melbourne, Rio de Janeiro, San Francisco, London, Hamburg...

"The new machines are automatic," Mr. Wu explained. "In ten days when everything is in place, we shall be producing fifty thousand corsets a day. And with only forty workers, just like before when we only turned out twelve thousand corsets. Come along and meet the engineer, Mr. Tsu."

The end of summer seemed to promise a period of calm for the responsible authorities. Leslie was dozing over the diplomatic dispatches and taking a daily swim at the Ladies' Recreation Pool; his friend Peterson had gone on home leave in Sussex; Graham devoted himself to golf at Fanling, where he had taken a room for the week; MacIntosh was familiarizing himself with new duties, which permitted him to forget Miss Orchid, at least during the day; Thompson was getting bored in the service but finding life outside it enormously amusing, thanks to the nurses at the King George Hospital; George Bennett was glued to his bench in the courtroom; Colonel Gwynn was in pursuit of a *Papilao Aeacus,* a specimen of which had been captured for the first time in April 1952; Mr. Crabb was off sailing.

Speaking of which, a disagreeable experience had occurred involving Mr. Crabb. The R.H.K.Y.C. had invited the crew of the Manila Yacht Club to a Sunday race. Mr. Crabb, the white hope of the local sportsmen, was sailing a Star. He was well in advance of the Philippine contestant and had more than a mile to cover. His victory would return the Western Pacific Cup to the clubroom, presented by Commodore Sir Bernard Leighton-Parker, K.C.B.

Crabb was rounding Shau Kiwan Point with one eye on the American aircraft carrier of 45,000 tons that was pulling out of the port and the other eye on the rival Star, which had been maneuvering for a moment to catch him up-wind. It was at this point that an extraordinary incident occurred: the crew of the aircraft carrier lined up on the flight deck and let out a triple hurrah while waving their caps. Mr. Crabb naturally looked about him to find what high personage the salute was addressed to. Surely not to the four junks anchored near the Point? So it must be for him. Mr. Crabb gallantly came up into the wind and responded with a wave of his own cap. And so it was that the Manila Yacht Club kept the Western Pacific Cup.

"I should have known," Mr. Crabb complained bitterly at the bar of the R.H.K.Y.C. "It was a ruse of the Americans to make the Philippines win. Trust them to be tricky."

It was in this peaceful atmosphere that the storm broke: on September 12, 1953, at 3:22 p.m. Mr. Kao, the headwaiter at the Seaview Hotel, informed Detective Ch'en confidentially that Pang Fen-tien was planning to lease the warehouse at Wanchai. He had asked Mr. Kao to invite the owner to lunch the next day and to give instructions to the staff to be generous with the Mei Kwei Lo, the rose-petal liqueur. Thompson advised cool-headedness. That was what he told Chief-Inspector Graham, whom he finally contacted by telephone about six o'clock.

"I don't intend to get worked up, but I don't like the look of it," said Graham.

"Don't worry, sir. There's no reason for Pang to get excited. Things are going very well on the junks. Just stay at Fanling. If anything important comes up, I'll call you right away; you can count on me."

Graham played badly the next day, losing three new balls on the first nine holes.

"That's because you muffed the first drive," said his wife sympathetically. "You'll see. It'll go better this afternoon."

"Order lunch, darling. I'll telephone to Thompson and join you."

Thompson still was reassuring.

"Everything's quiet, really, sir," he insisted. "Pang has signed a six-month lease for the warehouse."

"What's he up to, do you know?"

"He undoubtedly thinks that the water will have become too cold for bathing a month from now, that's all. He must be looking to the future."

"Have you spoken to MacIntosh about it?"

"Yes, just now, sir. It was he who furnished the explanation."

"And Inspector Chao, has he seen Pang?"

"He can't get hold of him. But go on playing in peace, chief. I'm keeping a lookout."

At lunch, Graham, who had remained silent since the barley soup, brusquely announced to his wife that he was returning to town.

"I'm going back with you," she said.

"No, darling, I'm just dropping into the office this afternoon. See you this evening."

Headquarters was plunged in a heavy torpor accentuated by the purring air conditioners. Thompson was out. Thanks to his secretary, Yen, Graham found the latest dossier on Pang. As well as the information Graham already had, it contained a note from Detective Li, dated the morning of September 15.

Li had seen Pang in a Palm Beach suit waiting at the airfield for the plane from Manila, with a car and chauffeur. He met three Filipinos, took them to the Hotel Miramar, and installed them in rooms 28, 29 and 30, then whisked them off to lunch at a restaurant on the Peninsula, to which Li was unable to follow them. One of the waiters later informed him that they had discussed contracts, in terms of hundreds of thousands of dollars, and that Mr. Pang had paid the bill.

Graham grabbed the phone and called his wife at Fanling:

"I've got to stay, darling. No, don't come back. It's too hot in town, I'll get along alone."

He resumed the direction of operations. High time.

On September 16, the warehouse had been emptied and a dozen masons were put to work. Messrs. Magalog, Lopez and Martinez (the names of the visitors from Manila) flew back home.

On September 17, a cablegram from Manila informed Chief-Inspector Graham that Messrs. Magalog, Lopez and Martinez, members of the governing committee of the Philippine Socialist Party, were known to be businessmen with considerable capital. Detective Li reported that Pang had dined at the Seaview with Lin, his former partner at the Lido.

On the eighteenth, Li reported that Pang was trying to sell his junks. Assistant Detective Ch'en, disguised as an employee of the Electric Company, had penetrated the former warehouse, which was being filled with seats, while decorators hung a great yellow curtain in front of a stage at one end and electricians tried out the lights.

On the same day, the cashier of the Trust Bank told Detective Liao that Mr. Pang had opened an account with a check for $300,000 signed by a certain Magalog. According to Assistant Detective Wang, Mr. Pang had asked a real estate agent to find him a house on the Peak at a price of $100,000. Mr. Lin had a telephone installed at the warehouse where he now made his permanent headquarters.

On September 19, the junks were sold to a shipping firm at Aberdeen (the fishing port near Hong Kong, named for one of the early Governors of the Crown Colony, not

Aberdeen, Scotland). Chief-Inspector Graham was summoned to the office of the Police Commissioner.

"What does all this mean?"

"First, here's the latest news, sir. Pang has had a sign made for the establishment. It's called the 'Gay Paris.'"

"A strip-tease theater?"

"I'm afraid so."

"So we're back where we started?"

"Pang Fen-tien doesn't seem to be actually running it. He left Diamond Hill this morning to occupy a house on the Peak. By the way, sir, if you have money to invest, I can give you a tip. Our friend Pang has bought $220,000 worth of shares in a beryllium mine in the New Territories. He went to the Stock Exchange with a bag stuffed with five and one-dollar bills."

On September 20, Inspector Chao called on Mr. Pang at his new house and Mr. Pang confirmed that he was out of show business to stay.

"And the 'Gay Paris?'"

"Just a little enterprise that he had originated and then sold to some Philippine impresarios. His friend Lin was to be the manager."

On September 21, about six in the evening, Mr. Pang's two junks were towed to the dock of their new owners at Aberdeen. The girls had barely time to have dinner, for the Gay Paris opened its doors at eight, with tickets costing fifteen dollars. Inside, there were three hundred seats, a Philippine orchestra and decorations de luxe. Graham, MacIntosh and Thompson, appropriately disguised thanks to the Special Branch, sat in the first row. The curtain came up on the corps de ballet dressed as Hakka peasant girls, with a single different detail: the black fringes on the hats came right down to their navels. So that when the dancers had taken off their blouses and pants, to the sound of "You Are My Sunshine," and with a sudden gesture had thrown their headdresses like flying saucers into the audience, the spectators came to their feet applauding madly and whistling. A single dancer had kept her hat on.

"Who's that?" asked Graham.

"Desert Cricket," whispered Thompson, ecstatically.

"How did you recognize her?" Graham asked suspiciously.

"Who else could it be? She'd have a hard time exhibiting herself completely nude with her rubber accessories."

"I don't see the tigress, Miss Orchid?"

Where, in fact, *was* Miss Orchid?

When the curtain finally came down at nine o'clock, Orchid had not been seen on stage. Detective Li reported to MacIntosh that she had quarreled with Pang Fen-tien. The quarrel, whose motive remained obscure, had taken place in front of her shack on Diamond Hill. She had slapped Pang in the face and retired, weeping, inside. Li had questioned Madame Hu and Assistant Detective Ch'en, but he still could not discover the reason for the quarrel.

September 22 was a Sunday. Between the fifteenth and sixteenth holes of the new golf course at Fanling, MacIntosh asked Graham what would happen to him if he were to marry a Chinese girl.

"Nothing special. You'd be assigned to somewhere outside Hong Kong, that's all. Why? Are you thinking of getting married?"

"It's just possible."

"Your play. You won the last hole."

On September 23 Inspector Chao burst into Chief-

Inspector Graham's office just at the hour of the weekly staff meeting.

"Pang Fen-tien's getting married tomorrow, and asked me to come. He said it would be an honor if you were to be present as well."

"At what time?"

"The reception's at his house at eleven."

"We'll be there, all of us, with pleasure. Don't you agree? By the way, Chao, who's the bride?"

"Miss Orchid. When I congratulated him, he said like a wise man, 'A man chooses a wife for her virtue, a concubine for her charm.' It looks to me as if he'd found both in the same woman."

"Pang can't be Chinese, he must be a Scot! The same woman for her virtues and her charm? How economical can you get? What have you got to say, you Scotsman over there?"

Graham noticed that the Scotsman, MacIntosh, had gone pale and was smiling in a really ghastly way.

"Some tea, Ian?"

"I may walk with a wise man for a thousand leagues, but eventually I must bid him goodbye."

—CHINESE PROVERB

Paris, 21 May 1964

My dear Bobo:

Just a story to revive your memories of old times, now that you're taking it easy at Hambledon.

I had just come out of the Embassy and was walking down the Rue du Faubourg Saint-Honoré when, in front of a particularly elegant furrier's, I ran into an old acquaintance—Mrs. Pang, or, if you remember her better under her maiden name, Miss Orchid.

You know what a bond there is among those who have been in the Far East together. We embraced each other, and she carried me off in her Bentley to the Plaza. Mr.—perhaps soon to be Sir—Fendrick Pang came to meet us in the lobby, with a London *Times* under his arm and asked us to have a Scotch in his rooms.

What were they doing in Paris?

"We're on the way to Canada and Uruguay," Mrs. Pang told me. "Once a year we make a trip around the world, Fendrick on business and I to look around."

"It's an expensive look," grumbled Mr. Pang. "What did you buy this afternoon?"

"Just a little leopard coat," said Mrs. Pang. "Four thousand francs. How much is that in dollars?"

"Do you remember how well my wife used to know how to count before we were married? Now she's completely forgotten. Just ask her how many children we have. I'm sure she doesn't know."

"How many?" I asked.

"Three boys and two girls. The last is only six months old."

"Impossible! How have you managed to keep your girlish figure?"

"That's what Ian MacIntosh asks me at every christening!"

"Good old Mac! How is he doing?"

"Still in Hong Kong. Recently he became Commissioner."

"Is he married?"

"No; he claims to be in no hurry."

"Ian's made great progress with his Chinese," she added, in an odd sort of *non sequitur*. "He's become quite devoted to his studies."

"And the 'Gay Paris'?"

"The 'Gay Paris'?" asked Mr. Pang, as if he had never heard of it.

"I've forgotten how to count," put in Mrs. Pang, "but my husband has lost his memory completely."

"Oh, yes, I remember," said Mr. Pang. "That's ancient history. Lin made it into a dance hall, but it didn't go too well. At present he's running my electronics factory."

"And Mr. Wu?"

(I don't know whether you remember Wu, Bobo. He was the founder of the Lido.)

"Honorary president of the Sons of Shantung. He exhibited his paintings last month, with considerable success. Lately he's set up a school for opera singers."

"My husband has been the real president for the last two years," put in Mrs. Pang. "They told me at the desk that Paris too has a Lido. Can we go there together this evening?"

I hastened to accept, but warned Mrs. Pang that it wasn't at all like its namesake in Hong Kong.

"I only hope it's heated," she said.

Mr. Pang slept all through the show.

Yours ever—
Leslie.

Hambledon, 26 May 1964

My dear Leslie:

What an amazing coincidence! I've just run into MacIntosh. A few days ago, on my way to take a plane to Le Touquet, where I was going to see the French admiral you may remember meeting at the bicycle taxi races, I found sitting next to me on the bus a tall fellow with black hair, a moustache and steel-rimmed glasses. On his knees he was carrying one of those wicker baskets they make only in Hong Kong. I struck up a conversation and soon found out that he was Commissioner Ian MacIntosh of the Royal Hong Kong Police. He told me he was going to Paris, Le Havre, New York, Canada and eventually Uruguay.

"For an investigation?" I asked him.

"No, for a holiday. I'm traveling for pleasure."

Now isn't that extraordinary?

Yours ever—
Bobo.